"You've a cold heart and no conscience!"

Saxon glared at her furiously as he went on, "I thought you were only extremely calculating in looking out for yourself, but when you demonstrate how you discard an old lover, I see your true character."

Debra was indignant. How dared he tell her how to conduct her personal affairs? "If I were coldhearted as you say, it wouldn't have taken me two months to break off with him. I don't like possessive men, and if that's coldhearted it's just too bad!"

"Precisely." Saxon's voice was icy. "Just don't bring any of your hardhearted philosophies to the farm or I'll send you packing!"

Debra felt frustrated. Saxon seemed to despise her for no reason. And yet for some unknown reason Debra longed to have his affection.

The Challenge

by

KERRY ALLYNE

Harlequin Books

TORONTO • LONDON • LOS ANGELES • AMSTERDAM
SYDNEY • HAMBURG • PARIS • STOCKHOLM • ATHENS • TOKYO

Original hardcover edition published in 1980
by Mills & Boon Limited

ISBN 0-373-02389-8

Harlequin edition published March 1981

CHAPTER ONE

THE Brisbane Royal Show! Debra Armitage had loved it ever since that day ten years ago when, for the first time, she had been fortunate enough to be included in the party taken from the orphanage. The crowds, the excitement, the thousands of exhibits, and the numerous pavilions filled with pedigreed animals of all breeds, shapes and sizes—she loved it all. But mostly it was the feeling of the country which reached out to her every succeeding year she had been lucky enough to be taken or, more recently, had paid the admission price herself, as she came through the turnstiles and once again stood on the concourse leading to the show ring.

The feeling was there in the exhibitions of farming machinery, the giant displays of primary produce, the livestock, and by no means least the farmers and graziers themselves—almost always uniformly dressed in fawn cord pants, white shirts and ties, and if that wasn't enough, there was the bush hat set well forward on sun-bronzed faces to finally distinguish the country born and bred from his city cousin. It was that once a year time when the primary producers of Queensland came to show and be judged on the fruits of their labours, and Debra wouldn't have missed it for anything.

At twenty-two years of age, her long dark hair swinging well below her shoulders, wide violet eyes outlined by thick black lashes and set in a piquantly heart-shaped face, she had long since left the orphanage behind her, but still she set aside this one day of the year for the Show. Even though this particular year was different from the rest in that three weeks ago the small firm for whom she had worked since leaving school had reluctantly been forced to close their doors owing to the prohibitive scale of rising costs and she, along with the rest of the staff, had found herself out of work, she still hadn't been able to resist the attraction.

It had been a worrying time since then, scanning the newspapers for a suitable position and finding none—where were all those jobs that had seemed so prolific only a couple of months ago?—and seeing her meagre savings dwindle rapidly as she went about her daily business of living without a wage to sustain her.

She supposed it had been an unwarranted extravagance to spend the day at the Show as she had done in previous years, but had consoled herself with a philosophical shrug of her shoulders and the thought that a few dollars either way wasn't going to make much difference if she couldn't find work within the next few weeks.

As the sun sank quickly below the city skyline and the myriad lights of the exhibition grounds sprang to sparkling life for the evening ahead, a chill wind began to whistle around the buildings, lifting discarded bags and paper refuse of all descriptions into lightweight missiles as it sent them whirling and scurrying down the roadways until they finally drifted to rest among others of their kind in ever mounting piles nestling in the corners and crevices of stairways and gutters.

Debra hugged her denim jacket closer to her slender form and wished she had thought to also bring a sweater with her to slip on over her thin cotton shirt, but the weather had been gloriously warm that morning when she had set out from the small bed-sitter she rented in Mortimer Terrace, with no hint of the keen invader which had just begun to blow.

Now she hurried along the roadway, intent on mingling with the crowds in the main ring to watch the rodeo events and so gain a little warmth from the nearness of the other spectators, past the swimming pools which had looked so inviting earlier in the day with their winking and blinking blue waters, but which now sent involuntary shivers down her spine at the thought of submerging in their cold depths.

It was then that she saw the little girl—eight years old, or nine at the most, dressed in pale blue jeans and a sunshine yellow polo-necked jumper, her dark pigtails flapping behind her as she chased a break-away red balloon which skipped and flew with the breeze in front of her. With hardly a hesitation she scaled the fence erected around the pools and, arms outstretched, made one final lunge to grasp the teasing novelty, slipped on the wet surrounds, and tumbled headlong into the shining water.

Debra rushed forward spontaneously, looking about her to see if there was anyone else who had witnessed the child's predicament, or if there was someone accompanying her, but these particular stands were closed for the night and there were

only a few people still making their way to the ring
on the far side of the walkway and no one who was
obviously trying to locate a missing child.

Pushing through the gateway, Debra dived into
the pool immediately she saw the girl come gasping
and flailing to the surface—a sure indication she
couldn't swim—and with a couple of strokes had
reached her side and clasped her under the arms.

'Whatever you do, don't panic, darling,' she urged
with a reassuring smile as she tossed her own stream-
ing hair back over her shoulders. 'Just hold on to
me and we'll have you out of here in no time.'

Either the child was too shocked to do anything
other than what she was told, or else she was an extremely cool-headed youngster—but for whichever
reason Debra was very grateful, for slim arms obedi-
ently twined around her neck and together they managed to inch their way over to the steps and out of
the water.

A few seconds later Debra had taken hold of a
small hand and led her charge back through the gateway just as a rather plump little woman wearing an
expensively tailored jersey suit came hurrying around
the corner, her fading blonde hair slightly ruffled
by the breeze and her blue eyes casting about her
worriedly. On seeing the two of them dripping with
water she came to a shocked standstill and spread a
hand agitatedly across her chest.

'Prue dear, whatever's happened to you? You
really shouldn't have gone rushing off like that,' she
scolded in distraught tones.

Contrite pixie brown eyes peeped upwards from
beneath spiky lashes. 'I'm sorry, Grandma, but the

wind blew my balloon away,' came the solemn explanation between bouts of shivering. 'Then I fell in the pool while I was trying to catch it and this lady,' she indicated Debra who was gritting her teeth in a supreme effort to stop them from chattering as the wind cruelly pierced her wet clothing, 'dived in and pulled me out.'

Two warm hands caught at one of Debra's cold wet ones. 'Thank heavens you were around, my dear!' Prue's grandmother gave a heartfelt sigh of gratitude. 'I can't tell you how appreciative I am. I couldn't have faced my daughter again if anything had happened to Prue.' She gave a shiver herself at the thought, but the sight of the two shaking forms before her soon had her returning to more immediate priorities with a bustling concern. 'But the pair of you must be frozen standing in this cold wind! This way,' she urged them lightly forward in front of her, 'I'm sure they'll have something to warm you at one of the first aid stations.'

By the time they had both been handed a hot drink and were wrapped in thick blankets, Debra began to feel a little less chilled as she sat on a bench next to Prue in the tent while they both cradled hot mugs between their fingers. After ensuring herself that they were as comfortable as possible under the circumstances Prue's grandmother turned to Debra with an apologetic smile on her lips.

'Goodness, I'm all a-dither! You must think me very discourteous, I haven't even introduced myself yet,' she said with a nervous fluttering of her hands, and proceeded to rectify the omission with a hurried, 'I'm Eleanor McAllister, and this is my granddaughter, Prudence Wayland.' A regretful look at Debra's saturated clothing and she continued, 'I'm terribly sorry we've spoilt your evening at the Show. You must let me make it up to you.'

Having given her own name in return, Debra discounted the suggestion quickly. 'Don't think about it, Mrs McAllister, it's not that important. I'm only pleased I was around to notice Prue when she fell in.'

Eleanor McAllister's eyes blinked rapidly. 'Oh, yes, otherwise there could have been very tragic consequences. How could I have told my daughter and son-in-law?' She shuddered dramatically before turning to her grandchild and wagging a finger at her remonstratingly. 'And I hope it taught you a lesson too, Prue. You really must keep away from swimming pools until you've learnt to swim, dear.'

A downcast head nodded dismally. 'Yes, Grandma,' Prue agreed dutifully before asking in an even more woeful tone, 'Does this mean we won't be able to see the rodeo and stunt motor-cyclists after all?'

Her grandmother stroked the damp hair back from her face consolingly. 'I'm sorry, darling, but you'll have to miss it tonight, I'm afraid. Perhaps we can come tomorrow night,' she offered in lieu.

'It's not held on Sunday night,' Prue reminded her disconsolately.

'Well, Monday, then.' Mrs McAllister was becoming a little flustered.

'Can Debra come too?'

The innocent question brought a hasty disclaimer from her rescuer. 'Oh, no, I can easily come another time on my own if I want to. There's no need for you to invite me to join you.'

Completely impervious to her protestations, however, Eleanor McAllister immediately agreed with her granddaughter. 'That's a very good idea. Of course she can come with us,' she concurred happily. 'After all, we do owe her a night out since we ruined this one, don't we?'

'Really, you don't have to do that, Mrs McAllister,' demurred Debra again in embarrassment. 'I can ...'

'But I'd like to, my dear,' Eleanor interrupted equably. 'I feel it's the least I can do to repay you in some measure for your prompt action. In the meantime, though, I think I'd better see about doing something to get you both back to the hotel before you catch your death of cold,' she concluded, walking to the tent opening.

'You don't have to bother about me, Mrs McAllister,' Debra began a protest once more. 'I don't live all that far away and I can catch a taxi.' A small lie since she didn't have the fare, but she didn't want Prue's grandparent thinking she was beholden to her for having retrieved her young relative from the pool.

'I couldn't let you do that!' Mrs McAllister sounded genuinely horrified at the idea. 'What would your parents think of me if I showed my gratitude by sending you home soaking wet? No, you must come back to the hotel with us and have your clothes dried first,' she insisted.

About to dissent for yet another time, Debra saw Prue's shoulders lift, an impish smile tug at her mouth and her head shake fatalistically, and she started to smile resignedly herself. Eleanor McAllister obviously wasn't about to be gainsaid!

Meanwhile, her self-appointed benefactor had

slipped out of the tent and called a white-coated official over.

'Bill, could you call a cab for me, please? Prue's had a slight accident and I'm taking her back to the hotel,' she explained. 'You might also let Saxon know where we've gone too when he comes out of the restaurant. He's attending the Breeders' Dinner there tonight and I told him we'd meet him afterwards.'

'Be glad to, Mrs McAllister,' the man agreed helpfully. 'And I'll go up to the office and ring for a taxi right away.'

The fact that Eleanor McAllister had mentioned a hotel had led Debra to surmise that the McAllisters might be visitors down from the country, but the easy familiarity with which the older woman had addressed the official—and his readiness in recalling her name—now had her wondering just *who* the McAllisters actually were!

In the taxi it was a constant battle to keep the water from spreading over the seats, although the blankets which Mrs McAllister had promised to return as soon as possible did absorb quite a large portion, but it was with relief that Debra felt the vehicle pull up on the marble gravelled forecourt of the imposing Panorama Hotel. Nothing but the best, she thought with a wry smile, and of course none other than that which had long been known as *the* city resting place for members of the grazing fraternity.

She was even more relieved when they had finally crossed the dimly lit foyer in their squelching shoes under the speculative eyes of the staff and a few lingering guests, and had reached the anonymity of the elevator which swiftly rose to the tenth floor and the extensive suite of rooms reserved by her companions.

An involuntary sneeze from Prue decided who would be using the bathroom first, and Eleanor McAllister hurried around making sure her grandchild had everything she needed and that she didn't take too long before being vigorously towelled dry and dressed in pyjamas and a prettily patterned dressing gown.

'Just hand me out your wet clothes when you're undressed and I'll ring for room service to have them dried,' Debra was instructed as she entered the bathroom in turn. 'Meanwhile, I'll find something warm for you to wear until they're returned.'

Debra smiled her thanks and closed the door behind her, only too pleased to be able to remove her wet and uncomfortable clothing, and especially her denim sandals which were beginning to rub her feet painfully. When she passed her clothes out to Mrs McAllister she was given in return a long pale blue silk nightdress, and a matching empress-line quilted housecoat with a high mandarin collar, which she accepted gratefully.

The streams of delightfully hot water from the shower dispelled her last feelings of coldness and after rubbing her hair as dry as possible she donned the provided night attire and padded back into the sitting room in bare feet.

Prue was laying full length on her stomach on the carpet, engrossed in an action-packed Western on the television, a plate of sandwiches and a glass of hot milk beside her. Eleanor, in the act of pouring a cup of coffee, returned the pot to its tray and hurried forward, picking up a blow dryer from the low table as she did so.

'Here, you dry your hair with this and I'll pour you some coffee,' she said, handing the brush to Debra while she bent and plugged the power cord into an outlet next to the tan and cream upholstered sofa. 'There's chicken and ham sandwiches here too if you'd like some. I had them brought up when the clothes were collected.'

Declining the offer of anything to eat, Debra sat down and switched on the brush, pulling it through the long fall of her hair while her hostess poured another cup of coffee and placed it in front of her together with the sugar and cream.

'I don't suppose your parents would have expected you home by now, anyway, would they?' Eleanor queried conversationally as she pulled her own cup closer and sank down on to the sofa. 'Although you can give them a ring if you would like to,' indicating the cream telephone on a table beside the television.

Debra switched the brush to the other side of her head before answering slowly. 'That's very kind of you, Mrs McAllister, thank you, but I live on my own. My—my parents are dead.'

Both sets, in fact, she pondered sadly. Her natural parents in a boating accident when she had been six and a sudden vicious storm had swept in from the horizon to catch them unawares, swamping their small craft in a matter of minutes, and leaving Debra as the sole survivor for the rescue boat to pick up because she was the only one they had ensured was protected by a lifejacket.

Then had come eighteen months in the orphanage until Matron and the doctor thought it advisable for adoption to take place, whereupon she had been taken into the loving hearts and home of Rose and Jack Armitage for a period of two wonderfully reassuring years, until they too had been callously wrested from her. There had been a storm that night as well—a circumstance which had produced many nightmares for Debra over the years whenever wild weather occurred—and the car in which they had all been travelling had been struck by a falling telegraph pole, crushing the front of the vehicle with ridiculous ease and sending Debra into a state of shock as the chilling scream of tortured metal grated on her ears as she had lain on the back seat.

After that there had been no more talk of adoption, neither the doctor nor Matron considering it prudent after two such traumatic disasters in her short life, and although her early experiences had left no physical scars the wounds went deep all the same, with the result that Debra had never again allowed anyone to become *that* necessary to her existence, and now made certain she kept her inner feelings and emotions very much on the defensive.

'Oh, my dear, I'm so sorry,' Eleanor brought her out of her reverie sympathetically, a compassionate hand patting her arm. 'You must find it very lonely. Have you no other close family?' And upon receipt of a negating gesture, 'Even though there are so many people in the city they do tend to be such impersonal places. Everyone's so busy rushing about and looking after their own business, they never seem to have time for anyone else. Although I look

forward to coming down to Brisbane every year for
the Show, I have to admit that after a fortnight I'm
only too ready to return home again.' She gave a
small pleased smile at the thought, but immediately
followed it with a doubtful, 'But, this time, only if
I can get some satisfaction from the employment
agency on Monday. I've been doing the rounds of
them for the past week and they still haven't been
able to find anyone suitable, so I'm beginning to
doubt whether I'll have any better success on my last
few days here.'

'It must be very frustrating when you only have
such a short time to hire someone,' commiserated
Debra, thankful that the conversation had veered
away from more personal topics.

'How true! You have no idea how hard good
staff is to come by in the bush these days,' Eleanor
informed her in a resigned tone. 'I've been adver-
tising in Acacia Crossing, and just about all points
north, south, east and west, for over a month now
without results, and it isn't even as if it's what you
would call an exacting position. Secretarial mainly—
shorthand, typing, a little book-keeping, that sort of
thing—with perhaps a couple of odd jobs thrown
in ... like driving Prue to and from school each day,
taking notes for me at some of my committee meetings, helping to prepare stud catalogues ...'

Acacia Crossing! That was in the Channel country
in the far west of the State. Debra stirred her coffee
pensively, an as yet only half formed idea coming to
light at the back of her mind.

'I suppose you're after someone who was born in
the country and has had first-hand knowledge of that

type of work,' she suggested diffidently.

Eleanor took a sip of her drink and shook her head emphatically. 'My dear, at the moment I feel I would be willing to settle for anyone who knew the difference between a typewriter and a calculator, no matter where they were born. It's just that with my committees and such I don't have time to help Saxon myself.' She paused, then smiled with twinkling honesty, 'Besides which, I just don't like office work.'

A responding smile caught at Debra's soft mouth, bringing a sparkle to her long-lashed eyes before they clouded again and she proposed hesitantly, 'I don't suppose you'd care to—er—give *me* a try ... would you?'

'As Saxon's and my secretary, you mean?' Eleanor queried with a frown, looking somewhat taken aback.

Now that she had actually made the suggestion and seen Eleanor's reaction Debra found herself wishing that she had left well alone. Just because her companion confessed to experiencing some difficulty in finding someone suitable there was no reason to believe that she was ready to accept just anybody for the post. Now, with a deprecatory lift of her shoulders, she chewed at her bottom lip doubtfully.

'Well—yes—that was what I meant,' she finally conceded in low, apprehensive tones. 'I know I've never worked anywhere but in the city before, and —and my shorthand is only of my own devising—I was never actually taught one of the accepted forms,' she admitted truthfully, glancing at Eleanor to gauge her response to such generous candour. 'However, I do have references to say I'm a competent typist and clerk. Not that I'm attempting to have you

believe I'm the best available, of course, but at
least I've always tried to be conscientious and I've
never received any complaints about my work,'
she concluded with a shy, self-effacing smile.

The face of the woman next to her cleared almost
magically. 'But of course you can have the job,
Debra, if you think you'd like it,' she exclaimed happily. 'If that's the type of work you've been doing I'd
be only too pleased to have you come and work
for us. But aren't you already employed?'

For the first time since being out of work Debra
was pleased to be able to answer in the negative. 'As
a matter of fact, I'm not at the moment,' she revealed.
'Up until three weeks ago I was employed at a
small manufacturing works not far from where I live,
but with prices and the cost of labour going so high
these days the owner couldn't compete with the larger
concerns and he had to either shut down or face the
likelihood of going bankrupt. Naturally, he chose
the former,' she shrugged understandingly.

'That's marvellous!' cried Eleanor, and placed
her cup and saucer on the table with an enthusiastic
clatter. 'Not about the poor man having to shut
down, of course,' she was quick to disclaim, 'but
that you're free to start immediately. You'll be able
to come back with us when we leave during the
week.' Here a rueful smile pulled at her lips. 'Although I expect Saxon will have some extremely
pertinent remarks to make about my precipitance in
engaging someone without the benefit of an agency's
recommendation. But then I'm used to lectures on
my impulsiveness,' she smiled again, unconcernedly
this time.

'You're sure you wouldn't rather wait until you've had a word with him about hiring me, Mrs McAllister? Until I can show him my references?' Debra asked anxiously, not wanting to cause trouble between Eleanor and her husband, and preferring to start off on the right foot herself.

'No, dear, of course not! I only meant it in fun,' Eleanor hastened to dismiss the worried look from her face. 'Saxon usually allows me a free hand in these affairs and I'm sure he'll be as pleased as I am to have finally got the matter settled so satisfactorily. Nevertheless, there is one thing you'll have to change.' A warm friendly smile dispelled any wariness her words may have created. 'You'll have to stop calling me Mrs McAllister and make it Eleanor instead,' she instructed. 'We're just not that formal in our part of the world.'

Unaware that there had been an interested spectator for the latter part of their conversation, and preventing Debra from immediately replying to Eleanor's behest, the two on the sofa now found Prue swivelled around on the floor to face them as she enquired interestedly,

'Is Debra going to live with you now because she pulled me out the the pool, Grandma?'

'Not exactly for that reason, dear,' the older woman laughed. 'But because Saxon and I need someone to help with the office work and so forth now that Noreen's left, and Debra has come to my aid—once again—by suggesting that she take over in her stead. You'll like that, won't you, because it will be Debra driving you to school each day now.' And she explained for Debra's benefit, 'Prue's staying with us for the next three months while my daughter and her husband, who are both doctors, are attending some important seminars and conferences overseas in connection with their medical research.'

'Mmm, I'll like that,' acceded a pleased Prue before turning back to her absorbing film, but managing to forgo its pleasures for a few moments longer in order to add over her shoulder, 'The last time I was out there all Noreen could do was to tell me to be quiet and stop talking all the way to town. You won't do that, will you, Debra?'

'No, I won't do that,' came the smiling concurrence. 'In fact, I'll probably have to ask you for directions because I won't know the way.'

'Oh, that's easy,' Prue discarded such a problem airily. 'You just turn left at the main gate and keep on that road for the next seventy miles. You can't get lost,' she finished absently, the television screen inexorably claiming her full attention once more.

A gulp and a weak smile were all Debra could summon in return for this casually imparted piece of information. She *could* drive, of course—Matron had helped her to get a licence during her last year at the orphanage and had allowed her to use the Home's vehicle on rare occasions after that—but seventy miles was probably the sum total of the distance she had driven to date, and she could only hope that her driving ability was such that she could safely transport Prue into town and back again each day.

Moments later she ran experimental fingers through her hair and switched off the brush. 'I think

it's just about dry now, thank you very much ...
Eleanor,' she murmured gratefully, and watched as
the other woman prepared to return it to her bedroom.

She had only just disappeared from view when the
door to the hallway opened and a man walked into
the room, his air of rugged masculinity making
Debra's indigo eyes widen in amazement. Surely this
wasn't Eleanor's husband! Why, he couldn't be more
than thirty-three or four at the most, she guessed.
She had been expecting someone much older.

As her glance travelled the powerful line of him
back to his suntanned face and her vision encoun-
tered an interested and appraising pair of eyes beneath a wide forehead and gold streaked dark blonde
hair, she suddenly remembered the mode of her dress
and her cheeks flushed warmly as she unconsciously
hugged the housecoat about herself more closely. It
was a strong, good looking face returning her inspection, the eyes a clear blue and ringed by surprisingly
dark lashes, the nose well formed, the mouth wide
and curving, the chin square and assertive.

Successful, determined, self-assured, and disastrously attractive to the opposite sex, were all descriptions she abruptly found herself applying to the tall
stranger, but for some unknown reason the minute
those thoughts flashed through her mind an entirely
different feeling surged through her body—one of
instinctive challenge—and to her absolute amazement she discovered her own chin to be inclining
upwards and her eyes defying his even before he had
time to utter a single word.

On hearing the door close Prue swung round once again, but this time scrambled to her feet and rushed across the room excitedly.

'Saxon! Did they tell you that I fell in the swimming pool and could've drowned if Debra hadn't come in after me?' she relayed her adventure happily now that she was safe and dry again. 'We had to come home in our wet clothes all wrapped up in blankets.'

He smiled down tolerantly at the animated face, his large hand resting affectionately on her shoulder. 'You were lucky there was someone around to help you,' she was told in a deeply smooth voice. 'I hope you thanked—Debra—for her timely assistance.'

Prue glanced towards the girl on the sofa and back again, a slight frown puckered her forehead as she tried hard to remember. 'I think I did ... but I know Grandma did if I didn't.' She tugged hard at his wrist to ensure she had his full attention before divulging her most impressive piece of knowledge. 'And now Debra's going to live with you at Wyeera.'

'Is she?' he counter-questioned in a slow drawl, along with a sardonic look at Debra which had her colour deepening furiously as his mouth took a decidedly cynical turn. 'How convenient! And in return for only one good deed too.'

By her puzzled expression it was clear the conversation was passing over Prue's head, but it definitely wasn't going over Debra's and she jumped to her feet in embarrassed confusion.

'It wasn't—it isn't—quite as it sounds, Mr McAllister,' she stammered and clenched her hands into stormy fists at the mocking look of disbelief she received in response to her statement. But before she could explain further Eleanor made her reappearance in the sitting room doorway.

'Ah, Saxon, you're back. Have you met Debra yet?' she smiled, and when it became evident that no such initiation had been made, went on, 'Debra, I'd like you to meet my stepson, Saxon. Debra Armitage.'

Which solved the relationship riddle that had been puzzling Debra for the last five minutes, but which introduction she acknowledged with only the barest movement of her head in return for his even briefer nod.

'I've hired Debra as our new secretary so she'll be coming home with us when we go,' Eleanor continued rapidly, and causing Debra to wonder if she was trying to pre-empt any objections he might raise. 'Or has Prue already told you all the news?' With a knowing smile for her young grandchild.

'Prue had already informed me in an—er—roundabout way,' he admitted in a lazy tone, cool eyes flickering speculatively over Debra's stiff housecoated figure. 'And is Debra also staying here with us until that time?'

'No, I'm not, Mr McAllister!' The words burst forth from her with a burning resentment for the construction he was choosing to place on her presence. 'It was only at Eleanor's insistance that I came to the hotel at all. Immediately my dry clothes are returned to me I shall be on my way,' she took pleasure in telling him tartly.

'I couldn't possibly have allowed her to go home

dripping wet,' his stepmother added her own point of view. 'Especially not after having spoilt her night out for her.'

'So we're taking her again on Monday night,' Prue revealed yet another of her items of importance, and promptly gave a sneeze.

'It doesn't sound as if you'll be going anywhere on Monday night,' Saxon grinned at his niece's woebegone expression. 'In fact, young lady, I think it's high time you were in bed.' He swung her up in the air and she clung to him piggy back fashion. 'Otherwise you won't have recovered enough to come to the Lion Safari tomorrow.'

Prue's eyes rounded with delight. 'Are we really going to see the lions?' and without waiting for an answer, 'Are Grandma and Debra coming too?'

Immediately Debra was shaking her head in a vehement denial, while Eleanor laughed after the retreating figures as Saxon carried his burden into the bedroom, 'No, your uncle can take you this time. After the walking I did with you at the Show this afternoon I shall enjoy having a rest tomorrow.'

'Oh, okay,' the happy acquiescence came floating back to them. 'I'll be able to tell you all about it when we get home instead.'

With a thoughtful expression on her face Debra picked up Prue's glass and plate from the floor and placed them on the table as Eleanor reseated herself on the sofa.

'Eleanor? I hope you didn't think it was an imposition for me to ask if I could be your secretary's replacement,' she spoke her anxieties aloud.

'Good gracious, no! I was only too pleased to accept your suggestion.' Suddenly she smiled in understanding. 'You're concerned about Saxon's reaction, is that it?'

'Well, he didn't seem exactly overjoyed with the idea,' Debra recalled ruefully.

'But only because I'd sprung another of my surprises on him, that's all. Not for any other reason,' Eleanor was quick to assure her.

Debra only wished she could feel as confident as her companion sounded. To her mind there had been other emotions, besides surprise, evident in the facial expressions and voice tones of Saxon McAllister, but before she could put her suspicions into words a knock sounded at the door which proved to be room service returning the dried and pressed clothes, together with the freshly laundered blankets.

Gratefully gathering her own apparel, Debra forsook any further conversation in order to hurriedly slip into the bathroom where she stripped off her borrowed raiment and dressed swiftly in her own, and feeling far more assured and secure once she had done so, and grimacing as she slid her reluctant feet into her still damp and cold sandals. With Eleanor's carefully folded clothes draped over one arm she returned to the sitting room and, to her misgiving, found that Saxon had apparently been prevailed upon to drive her home himself when she noticed him withdrawing a car key-ring from his pocket.

Deliberately ignoring him, she turned to his stepmother. 'Thank you very much for the loan of the dry clothing, Eleanor,' she said appreciatively.

'Now, if I might use the phone, I'll ring for a taxi and take myself out from under your feet.' This last for the benefit of the man behind her.

'There's no need for that, the car's only just down-stairs,' a deep voice cut in firmly.

Debra sent him a smile of gibing sweetness. 'I wouldn't dream of putting you to such trouble at this late hour, Mr McAllister. So, if I could ...'

'But of course Saxon will drive you home, dear,' in-serted Eleanor this time. 'It's no trouble at all, is it, Saxon?' She looked to her stepson for confirmation.

'Not if we don't stand around here discussing it for the rest of the evening,' he conceded with a drawl-ing kind of impatience.

'See? Saxon doesn't mind,' she laughed, and walked to the door beside Debra. 'And we'll pick you up on Monday night for the Show at about— hmm, seven, I think—if that's all right with you.'

Debra stopped moving and swung to face her. 'Really, Eleanor, there's no need for you to take me with you on Monday,' she protested anxiously, and attempting to prove to the man behind them that it hadn't been her idea that she accompany them. 'Miss-ing tonight's events just wasn't that important.'

The other woman had different ideas, however. 'But I have to see you some time to make final ar-rangements about you coming home with us, so it might just as well be at the Show,' she proposed lightly.

Faced with this seemingly incontrovertible logic there was nothing for Debra to do but give in, which she did with as much enthusiasm as she could man-age. Not that she didn't want to meet Eleanor, but rather because if it could possibly have been avoided she would have preferred not to endure an evening laced, as she was sure it would be, with Saxon McAllister's somewhat disparaging innuendoes. The less contact she had with the man the better, and for more reasons than one, as far as she was concerned.

Her goodbyes said, she accompanied him to the elevator in silence, thanking her lucky stars that it was stationary on the floor above and didn't take long to reach them. After they entered the softly lit cubicle Debra watched covertly as Saxon pressed the appropriate button for the underground parking station with a strong brown finger, her thoughts involuntarily recalling the dissatisfaction he had displayed on learning of Eleanor's decision to hire her, and perturbingly creating last-minute doubts as to whether she had done the right thing by accepting.

She could, of course, just telephone in the morning and say that she had changed her mind, even though she believed at least Eleanor and herself could work well together, but—catching frosty eyes surveying her thoroughly and not a little derisively—wasn't that exactly what *he* wanted? Inexplicably just the thought of the smug pleasure it would probably afford her companion should she let him coerce her into yielding was enough to have her squaring her shoulders and returning his gaze defiantly. Come what may, she was going to keep the position Eleanor had given her, whether Saxon liked it or not!

CHAPTER TWO

SECONDS later the elevator doors opened automatically to the view of a low roof, concrete stanchions, and rows of neatly parked vehicles of every colour and description. Debra preceded Saxon from the compartment and stood waiting for him to indicate in which direction they should proceed, then, when he started off down the right-hand lane with a long supple stride, found it necessary to break into a trot every so often in order to keep pace with him. That was, until her damp sandals began chafing again, and she lagged behind so she could lessen the friction by moving more slowly. It was a moment before she realised he had stopped and was waiting for her, hands resting lightly on lean hips, his expression unfathomable.

'I'm sorry if I was walking too fast,' he apologised, but to Debra's mind sounding as if he wasn't experiencing the slightest touch of remorse at all.

She shrugged indifferently. 'It wasn't that. It's just that my sandals are still wet and they're rubbing my feet.'

Now his expression was all too clear. It was definitely mocking. 'Sorry, sweetheart, but you'll find I'm nowhere near as obliging as my dear, unquestioning stepmother. I have no intention of offering to carry you,' he gibed hatefully.

Debra drew in a sharp infuriated breath. As if she

would *want* to be carried by the likes of him! Her violet eyes flashed indignantly as she bent to wrench the discomfiting footwear from her feet.

'Oh, don't worry, Mr McAllister, I can assure you no such thought crossed my mind. It would never occur to me to suppose you capable of such a gallant act,' she smiled caustically as she stormed past him on bare feet until she was some yards ahead, whereupon she swung back to face him, a sandal-dangling hand perched on each of her own hips this time. 'Not that I'd wish to be accused of rushing you, of course, but ...' a nod of her head indicated the rest of the cars in the line and she demanded pertly, 'which one's yours?'

Even after they had driven up the ramp and had joined the rest of the vehicles traversing the city streets Debra's heartbeat was still suffocatingly fast and hard against her ribs as she remembered the savage look on Saxon's face when he had paced towards her in the parking area. For a time she had wondered if he intended removing the provoking look from her face physically—making her quail at the thought—but he hadn't, fortunately, he had merely pushed past her in tight-lipped silence to unlock and drag open the passenger door of a white sedan, then had proceeded to slam it ruthlessly shut only seconds after she had nervously slipped in front of him and on to the dark green leather seat.

Seeing only her own worried reflection when she stared out of the side window she turned her head to the front, her fingers intertwining agitatedly in her lap. This was no way to start with a new employer. If she was really honest perhaps she could admit that maybe—but only maybe—Saxon did have some justification for his behaviour. It must have seemed very suspicious for him to return to the hotel and find that Prue's rescuer was already ensconced as a member of his staff. Perhaps she should have tried a little harder to explain the circumstances instead of taking umbrage as she had. Impulsively she twisted in her seat to face him, speaking quickly, before her courage failed her.

'Look, Mr McAllister, I'd like to explain about . . .'

'*Don't bother*, Miss Armitage! I'm not interested!'

His interruption was uttered with such harsh finality that she slumped back dejectedly, her thoughts turning despairingly inwards again. It was no use, she sighed quietly, he was determined to . . .

The sudden blaring of an impatient car horn behind them had her glancing up curiously when she realised they weren't moving, even though the traffic lights at the crossroads directly in front of them were green, and she swung a puzzled look towards the man next to her. His eyes never wavered from the windshield, but she surmised he must have sensed her baffled interest because she could see the corner of his mouth beginning to edge upwards satirically.

'How about you keep your mind on one thing at a time, Miss Armitage, or have you forgotten you're supposed to be doing the navigating? You did say we turned at this set of lights, didn't you?' he enquired goadingly.

For revenge Debra was tempted to refrain from telling him until the drivers behind them were really irate, but the glittering gaze she intercepted dissuaded her from this course of action.

'Turn right, and then first on the left,' she told him hastily, deducing that it wouldn't be at all smart to ride Saxon McAllister too hard unless one was extremely confident of what his reaction was likely to be. In his anxiety to be rid of her she wouldn't put it past him to drop her off at the next convenient corner and leave her stranded. Her statement at the hotel about ringing for a taxi had been pure bluff.

One thing she was certain of, though, she had no intention of apologising for not having previously advised him of the direction they should take at the lights. The last time she had attempted to apologise for a misunderstanding she had been very curtly squashed. She wasn't going to put herself in such a position again!

Presently she was pointing out the old terrace house where she lived and which had been converted into small bed-sitters capable of accommodating half a dozen single tenants. After the gracious refinement of the Panorama Hotel it was difficult to see the time worn building with anything but critical eyes. The stonework was pitted and dirty, the railing fence had obviously seen better days, and the drab curtains at the windows offered no promise of any improvement inside.

As soon as the sedan pulled up beside the curb Debra hurried to free herself from the seatbelt and thus preclude the necessity for her escort to emerge from the car, but the belt proved stubborn to her unpractised manipulations and by the time she had finally extricated herself from within its confines Saxon was already holding the door open for her to alight. She did so in a rush, scooping up her sandals from the floor in one hand, and immediately making for the house even as she thanked him perfunctorily for the lift. She was equally anxious as he was for them to part company.

There was no chance for him to reply, however, for another figure suddenly appeared from within the shadows of the darkened porch and she sighed despondently to hear an all too familiar voice complain in a softly hurt tone, 'I've been waiting here for you since eight-thirty, Deb. Why didn't you let me know you wanted to go out tonight? You know I would have taken you.'

Errol Pemberton! Why did it have to be *this* night that he turned up for another of his rejection scenes? Debra had dated him a number of times some months ago, but there had never been anything serious on her part, so when he started to become extremely possessive she had thought it best to call the whole thing to a halt. Unfortunately, this was easier said than done with someone of Errol's unfaltering persistence. Not terribly tall, lean and brown-haired, he sometimes reminded her of a terrier, for once having got his mind set on something there was no way he was going to abandon it again without a long and furious tussle. So far she had tried to get her message across without hurting his feelings too much, but now she was beginning to wonder whether he had any sensitivity to *be* gentle with!

A pointed glance for Saxon McAllister failed in its intention to let him know his presence wasn't required in such a personal matter, for he appeared disposed to ignore the mute hint, because he only leant back more comfortably against the car with his arms folded across his broad chest and an annoyingly amused look on his face. With an inward groan Debra turned her back on him, a slightly nervous hand flicking her long hair back over her shoulder, a major effort required to keep her voice cool and controlled.

'I'm sorry you've had a wasted evening, Errol, but I did tell you the last time you rang that I wouldn't be seeing you again,' she reminded him steadily.

'But what went wrong, Deb?' You know I love you, and we were so right together.' His voice grew stronger as he began to repeat his habitual claims.

Debra paired her sandals in one hand and thrust the other into the front pocket of her jeans, hoping it would give her an air of unassailable conviction. 'But I don't love *you*, Errol,' she tried to impress on him decisively, all too conscious of the indolent figure at the curb. 'Sure, we had some good times together, but you can't expect them to go on for ever. I'm sorry, but you just weren't right for *me*!'

The dark brown eyes which had been shaded in the hazy glow from a street lamp two doors away suddenly lost their soulful quality and, to Debra's surprise, became almost rancorous.

'He is, though, I take it?' he questioned bitterly, his head nodding past her to indicate the third presence. 'What's he got that I haven't ... more money?'

'No, of course not!' she denied promptly, but when an unconscious sideways glance from beneath curling lashes showed one of Saxon's brows to be ironically challenging her statement, she flushed and amended wryly, 'Well ... probably. Although that has nothing whatever to do with ...'

'Hasn't it?' Errol's disbelieving query cut across her denial swiftly. 'Then it must be something just as rewarding, otherwise he wouldn't be bringing you home in such disarray!'

'Oh, don't be so damned ridiculous!' she snapped back at him in embarrassment, knowing full well that Saxon could hear everything that was being said. 'I'm not wearing my shoes because they're wet!'

'Huh! That's a good one,' he snorted sarcastically. 'Especially since it hasn't rained for the last three weeks. I suppose your make-up was washed off in the same fanciful but convenient shower, was it?'

'No, in mine, actually. At my hotel,' came the bland intervention which had both of them staring speechlessly at the newly approaching figure, one in wide-eyed dismay, the other in a return to sorrowful wretchedness.

Debra was the first to break the tension-filled silence, but not until she had given Saxon McAllister a wrathful glare which should have felled him to the ground.

'There was no need to say that!' she hissed at him furiously. And to Errol, in an attempt to dismiss the implied inference, 'It wasn't anything like you're imagining. He's just my—my new employer ...'

'In a manner of speaking only,' Saxon again put in a sardonic-sounding correction, and it was only his clasping his arms firmly around Debra's shoulders and pulling her back to rest immovably against his muscular shape that stopped him from being dealt a stinging slap from his absolutely incensed captive when he went on to add implicitly, 'Although she will be moving in with me next week.'

One look at the size and height of the man confronting him and Errol knew he was beaten. Not that it had ever been his way, but he wasn't such a fool as to resort to physical arguments with someone who made him feel a puny dwarf.

'So it's all settled, then,' he murmured defeatedly, and had a strangled noise issuing from Debra—the only sound the pressure of Saxon's forearms would allow as they lay against her throat.

Her struggles to be free of the enveloping embrace when she saw the look of hopelessness descend over Errol's face as he turned away were unexpectedly, but efficiently, stilled by Saxon suddenly spinning her around and his hard hands cradling her cheeks.

'There's no point in keeping it a secret, sweetheart,' he proposed softly, holding her somewhat bemused gaze steadily, but not too bemused to note that he said it clearly enough for Errol to hear. 'It is all arranged that you're coming home to Wyeera next week, isn't it?'

The aggravating lift to the corners of his mouth had her glaring at him and renewing her attempts to pull free in order to explain, but he apparently had no intention of allowing this to happen, and to prevent her spluttered, 'You—you ...!' from eventuating into the onslaught it was evidently going to be, his firm lips closed over hers with a ruthless domination which effectively cut off her words and had her frantically endeavouring to break the surprisingly disturbing contact.

Except perhaps in order to annoy, Debra had no idea why Saxon should be going to such lengths to convince Errol there was some deeper relationship between them than actually existed, but the effect he was having on her emotions was quite illogical. When he finally released her she was quick to pretend a nonchalance she was far from feeling by looking anxiously around for Errol—only he was nowhere to be seen—and thereby giving her breathing a chance to resume its normal tempo. This proved to be only momentary because Saxon's next words had her pulse rate climbing alarmingly again.

'Earlier this evening I had thought you were only extremely calculating in keeping an eye open for the main chance,' he denounced bitingly, his eyes cold and contemptuous. 'But in truth you're nothing more than a cold-hearted, conscienceless little bitch! You weren't going to leave that poor devil any pride or self-respect, were you?'

Debra was so unprepared for his scathing words that for a moment she was too shocked to answer. But when she eventually did she hurled her own censures back fierily, her breasts rising and falling rapidly against the thin material of her shirt.

'*I* didn't leave him any pride or self-respect!' she repeated in stunned disbelief. 'Don't you think the shoe's on the other foot? I was under the impression it was *you* who saw to that with all your suggestive insinuations and presumptuous kissing!'

'By which means I at least left him with enough dignity to believe he'd been thrown over for someone else!' Saxon retorted icily. 'If you'd had your way you would have wiped the floor with him in your desire to prove you'd rather have no company than his!'

Debra's fingers curled about her sandal straps indignantly. How dare he have the audacity to tell her how to conduct her personal affairs!

'Of course I wouldn't have wiped the floor with him! If I had, maybe it wouldn't have taken me almost two months to break off with him,' she retaliated pungently, her eyes wide and sarcastic. 'But just because he thinks he's in love with me, it doesn't mean that I have to accept his company whether I want it or not. I don't happen to like possessive men, and if you consider that's being cold-hearted and conscienceless then it's just too bad, because that's the way I am!'

'Precisely!' he endorsed with an anything but pleasant smile. 'But if you're planning on bringing any of your hard-headed little philosophies to Wyeera, then I feel it only fair to warn you,' his voice sharpended and grew colder, if that was at all possible, 'that although Eleanor may have hired you, it will be me you'll be answerable to while you're on the property, and I don't appreciate my staff causing unnecessary upheavals. You catch my drift, Miss Armitage?' One well-shaped brow peaked expressively.

Up until that moment Debra had thought she would be in Eleanor's charge, and his revelation to the contrary caught her off guard. Although, she mused ruefully, if she had taken the trouble to think about the matter at all, it shouldn't really have come as such a surprise. Saxon McAllister wasn't the type to relinquish any of his authority on his own property, and especially not to a woman, not even if she did happen to be his stepmother. Determinedly she made her features relax into a tantalising smile and set about doing some warning of her own.

'I believe so, Mr McAllister,' she finally answered

his question, and refusing to let any of her inner turmoil show. 'However, if you thought that your little attempt at sabre-rattling was going to have me throwing up my hands in horror and charging for the nearest telephone to let Eleanor know I'd had second thoughts about accepting the position, then I'm afraid you're going to be very disappointed. You receiving *my* message, Mr McAllister?' she concluded with dry provocation.

Two broad hands were pushed into the back pockets of his pants and his dark blond head lowered in sardonic acknowledgment. 'How could I fail to? You make it so disgustingly obvious! Having caught Eleanor in a weak moment and feeling beholden to you for saving her granddaughter, you're far too coldblooded to surrender your advantage and miss out on an opportunity you apparently feel will be to your benefit just because of a few discouraging remarks from me. I do hope, though—for your sake,' and Debra really didn't care for the emphasis he stressed on those words, 'that you have the right qualifications for this post you've so eagerly acquired for yourself. Otherwise ...' Now it was his turn to smile, and the fact that it boded no good for herself still couldn't quite prevent her from appreciating the magnetism of his personality when the tautness left his expression and he looked as vitally attractive as he did at the moment. 'Otherwise, it's more than likely you could find yourself regretting the overly hasty decision you made tonight. I presume you've had previous experience on a cattle station, and that you're familiar with the work?' he quizzed mockingly.

Debra suspected he was as aware as she was that the work wouldn't be familiar in the slightest, but as she had no intention of telling him so to his face she merely hunched her slim shoulders offhandedly beneath her denim jacket.

'Office work is much the same anywhere, Mr McAllister, and Eleanor knows my qualifications. Why don't you ask her if you have any doubts?'

A forceful hand ensnared her chin before she had a chance to evade it. 'Never doubt that I won't, sweetheart.' He lowered his head to within inches of hers and had her catching a soft bottom lip apprehensively between her teeth at his unnerving proximity. 'But her replies had better be more commendable than yours, because I have a natural antipathy for sharp little females who think they only have to spin some pathetic hard luck story for everyone else to chivalrously overlook their inadequacies. So, believe me, those qualifications had better be good, or I'll make sure I'm personally responsible for turning your life into such a hell that you'll think I'm doing you a favour in accepting your willing resignation!' he revealed his ultimate objective inflexibly.

'Oh, is that so?' Debra gasped stormily as she twisted out of his hold. 'Well, unfortunately for you, I don't happen to give up that easily, so do your damnedest, Mr McAllister, and we'll see whether I hand in a willing resignation or not, won't we?' she gibed as she whirled for the steps leading on to the porch. And turning back to add in a tone which conveyed an overwhelming confidence which was actually non-existent, 'What's more, *I* don't like arrogant males who trade on their physical size and strength

in order to intimidate those smaller than themselves!
So perhaps you'd better watch out too, in case I decide to make your life such a hell that you'll think I'm
doing *you* a favour when I finally decide to leave!'

His eyes narrowed consideringly and he raised one
hand to sketch a taunting salute. 'Okay, sweetheart,
I accept your challenge ... but I also give you fair
warning.' He paused and his eyes wandered over
her waiting form slowly, mockingly. 'For someone
like you I won't necessarily be fighting fair or re-
putably, and you can take my word for it that there'll
be no concessions made because you're a female,'
he informed her meaningfully.

About to insert her key in the lock, Debra spun
round, her lips pouting impudently. 'You don't say!'
she jeered. 'But then, if allowances were to be made
because of my sex, you would first need to be a gentle-
man, and as I've already intimated once before this
evening, we both know you would never fit into that
category, don't we?' she smiled sweetly.

If Saxon intended to reciprocate he wasn't afforded
a chance to do so because the front door was suddenly thrown wide, spilling pale yellow light on to
Debra's surprised face, and a large woman positioned
herself in the middle of the opening.

'I'll have that key, thank you, young lady,' she
smirked triumphantly, and had snatched it out of
Debra's unsuspecting fingers before she could protest. 'I told you what would happen if you didn't
come up with your back rent in a hurry. Well, I re-let
your room today ... to someone who pays in advance!'

'B-but you can't do that!' Debra stuttered in her

mortification. It had been humiliating enough to have Saxon McAllister witness the scene with Errol, but this was even worse. 'I told you I'd pay you as soon as possible, Mrs Jenkins. As soon as I could get another job, and—and now I've got one.'

'You're too late!' The ring of satisfaction in the woman's tone was quite noticeable.

'Don't you have a lease?' queried Saxon sardonically, moving to Debra's side.

She shook her head despondently.

'I wouldn't give a lease to the likes of her,' Mrs Jenkins sneered spitefully. 'Madams like that give the place a bad name, what with all the men they bring round. There was one of them hanging about all this evening but I see she's apparently found herself other fish to fry. No, I wouldn't give her a lease, the only reason I let her have the room at all was because she found me in a weak moment and I felt sorry for her.'

'That's not true!' Debra burst out resentfully. Mrs Jenkins had never experienced a weak moment or felt sorry for anyone in her life. 'You practically begged me to take the room because, at the time, you couldn't find anyone else who would pay the rent you were asking for such dingy accommodation. I only agreed because you said you were going to improve it ... except that you never did.'

'You didn't have to stay,' the woman retorted smugly. 'No one was twisting your arm.'

Debra's shoulders slumped listlessly. 'Anything better cost even more.'

'It was good enough for you not to pay your rent for the last three weeks, though, wasn't it?' Mrs Jen-

kins bent forward, her small black eyes shining
maliciously. 'But don't think just because I've got
another tenant that it lets you off the hook, miss, because it doesn't. I'm impounding all your property
until I'm paid every last cent of what you owe me.
So now what have you got to say for yourself?' she
taunted.

'I—I ...' Debra couldn't believe it was all happening. She had set off that morning with nothing more
than an enjoyable day at the Show in mind, but since
then her whole world seemed to have been turned
topsy-turvy.

'How much?' Saxon entered the conversation
again, his voice ominously harsh, one hand going to
his hip pocket.

'No!' Debra reached out to stop him as she realised his intent. 'I don't want ...'

'What you want doesn't concern me in the slightest ... as I'm sure you'll discover before very much
longer!' he rasped as he shook her fingers away
roughly and brought forth a folded leather wallet.
'How much?' he demanded again of the woman before them.

Mrs Jenkins was only too pleased to tell him, but
added with relish, 'She still can't have her room
back, though.'

Saxon counted out and thrust a bundle of notes
towards her which she grasped eagerly. 'I doubt anyone in their right mind would want it back,' he derided contemptuously. 'But now I'll have Miss Armitage's luggage, if you please. All of it!' pointedly.

'Wait here,' they were ordered with a sniff before
she made her way down the hall. When she returned

it was with a case in each hand which were dropped carelessly on to the top step. 'Good riddance, I say! She's brought me and my poor husband nothing but trouble ever since she came here.'

'And just what did she mean by that?' Saxon enquired grimly as soon as the reverberations from the slammed door had died away.

Debra heaved one of the cases down on to the pavement. 'Her *poor* husband,' she said in acid accents, 'is a beer-guzzling lecher who considers all female tenants to be fair game.'

'So why *didn't* you move?'

'To where? The fire instead of the frying pan?' she rounded on him hotly. 'There hasn't been one bedsitter I've rented yet that didn't have some drawback. At least with this place being old it had solid doors and strong locks. I made certain he didn't get the opportunity to cause me too much worry.'

'So where are you going to stay now until we leave?' he asked, joining her on the pavement with her other case.

The fire died out of her swiftly, leaving her expression clouded with doubt. 'The Y.W.C.A. or somewhere similar, I suppose,' she shrugged, biting at her lip.

'Don't you have any money at all?'

'Only the twenty dollars I left in my room this morning.'

'Well, at a guess, I'd say you can kiss that goodbye,' he snorted cynically. 'That old harridan wouldn't have missed a trick when she was clearing out your room.'

'Oh, but surely she wouldn't ...' She stopped with

a despairing sigh. Oh, yes, Mrs Jenkins would take it if the chance presented itself. 'It looks as if it will just have to be one of the Missions, then, doesn't it?' she proposed with a valiant half laugh.

'No family anywhere in Brisbane?'

'No family anywhere ... period,' she grimaced dolefully.

Saxon ran a hand savagely through his hair and gave a smothered groan of irritation as he walked over to the car and pulled open the door. 'Get in,' he commanded, returning for her cases which he tossed on to the back seat.

'I'm sorry to be causing you such inconvenience,' Debra murmured apologetically, eyes downcast, after they had been driving for a few moments. 'Do you know where the Mission is?'

'No!'

At that flat denial her eyes flickered up to his coldly set profile in puzzlement. 'Then where—where are we going?' she asked hesitantly.

'Back to the hotel.'

'W-what for?'

'What the hell do you think for?' His words snapped out with the crack of a whip. 'To book you into a room, of course!'

'But you know I haven't the money to stay there,' she protested almost tearfully.

'Then let's say I figure it's the best way I know of protecting the investment I've already been forced into making in you,' he bit out corrosively.

His meaning was all too clear and she stared at him incredulously, furiously. 'You think I might just disappear now that I've had my debts cleared for me?' she gasped.

'Too bloody right I wouldn't put it past you to vanish into thin air immediately my back was turned! I don't trust you one little inch, sweetheart!' There was nothing at all endearing in the term.

'Then why pay my back rent at all?' she flared, smarting under his denigrating opinion. 'Surely that was your best solution for getting rid of me altogether.'

'What, and have you ringing Eleanor in the morning to tell her the pitiful tale so she could offer to pay it for you ... with no strings attached!' He laughed mirthlessly. 'Uh-uh! I much prefer it this way, with *me* calling the tune.'

'It will take me ages to pay it all back.' Debra could see her indebtedness to him looming for months ahead.

'Won't it?' he agreed with gibing mockery. 'However I did warn you that I wouldn't be making things easy for you. If you've already found you can't take it and want to cry quits, I'm quite amenable.'

'In other words, if I tell Eleanor I've decided against taking the job, then I don't have to reimburse you, is that it?'

'Just about.'

Debra held her breath and counted to ten in an effort to control her mounting fury. 'Then you really have misread my character, haven't you, Mr McAllister?' she stormed. 'I asked for that position because I needed it—I still do—and I can assure you I'm not about to be deprived of it by some arrogant damned male who thinks he only has to wave a few of his measly dollars under my nose to have me doing exactly as he wants! Oh, no, boss,' she used the word deliberately, 'you'll have to do better than that. You can't *buy* my resignation.'

Surprisingly, the retaliation she expected didn't eventuate. Instead, one corner of his mouth twisted obliquely and he taunted, 'You have no objection to said arrogant damned male buying your services, though, I take it?'

'Not at all,' she shrugged, her temper abating somewhat. 'My services are for sale ... my self-respect isn't.'

'You mean, after tonight's efforts you still have some?' he quizzed with acrid scepticism.

Debra might have known that half bantering mood was only momentary! 'Why not? I'm sure you have, even after your attempted bribe!'

'Not a bribe, Miss Armitage, an offer of severance pay,' he corrected with cool dryness.

'Made out of the kindness of your heart, I suppose?' she gibed.

'You could say that,' he agreed. 'I figured that if it saved my stepmother some future regrets then it would have been worth it.'

'And yet the reason you gave for taking me back to the hotel was that you didn't trust me not to disappear before I'd repaid what I owe you. Now you're offering it to me on a platter.' She shook her head in confusion. 'I don't follow your reasoning.'

'Then allow me to explain the fine difference.' Again that lazy curve to his lips took her unawares, setting her heart thumping in an uneven rhythm. 'It's my prerogative to *give* the money away, sweetheart, but I'm sure as hell not having you *take* it without my say-so! As I said, I mean to be the one dictating the shots where you're concerned, and that includes the circumstances surrounding the termination of your employment with the Wyeera Grazing Company.' He shot her an unbearably goading look. '*Now* do you understand my reasoning?'

She nodded with what she hoped would appear as unconcerned insouciance, but if it hadn't been for the fact that she needed work so desperately and that she knew Eleanor was on her side, Debra suspected she would have been seriously considering calling the whole thing off. The challenge she had issued so recklessly was already beginning to rebound with a vengeance!

'You're positive you wouldn't like to reconsider my offer?' Saxon enquired persuasively, almost as if he could sense her doubts.

It was just the type of remark she needed to have her sticking to her guns and dismissing her previous qualms. 'No, thank you, Mr McAllister, although I do appreciate your generosity,' she smiled with honeyed sweetness. 'I know what it must have cost you to make such a magnanimous gesture.'

The lights from the oncoming cars threw his glacial blue eyes into bold relief in the darkened interior of the vehicle, and she couldn't quite control an inward tremor of nervousness as he warned. 'In that case, perhaps you'd better tread a little more warily, Miss Armitage. I wouldn't like you to forget that it's my home ground where you'll be living.'

Determined that he shouldn't see just how that

knowledge affected her, Debra forcibly kept her smile in place. 'But if I do I'm sure you'll be only too pleased to remind me, won't you, boss?' she quipped pertly.

'You'd better believe it!'

She did. And as she followed him into the hotel a few minutes later there was only one thought sustaining her. Thank God for Eleanor! For without that woman's moderating influence she had no doubt her time spent working for Saxon McAllister would have been extremely uncomfortable, to say the least!

CHAPTER THREE

THEY left Brisbane's Archerfield Aerodrome four
days later with Saxon at the controls of his Beech-
craft Sundowner and on a heading of west by north-
west. It was the first time Debra had been in a plane
—there had never been the money nor a reason for
her to fly before—and she found the extended panorama provided below her not only beautiful but
interesting as well, especially the further west they
travelled.

As they passed over Brisbane the scene consisted
mainly of suburban homes, each set within its own
boundary fence, and a large majority of them
equipped with swimming pools, if those brilliant
patches of blue in back gardens were anything to
judge by. Then the outer perimeters of the city came
into view, the buildings set further apart now, the
fences marking off acres instead of perches. And so
it continued. The size of the properties progressively
becoming larger and larger as they moved into the
inland. Over the Downs the paddocks were measured
in their hundreds of acres, a little further out in their
thousands, until at last it just wasn't possible to make
out any boundaries at all and the homesteads were
very few and far between as they began to fly over
the myriad creek and river-veined landscape of the
Channel country.

An area often described as a Garden of Eden and

which could turn off huge numbers of prime cattle in good seasons, it could also be a harsh and forbidding region, as many early explorers had discovered to their cost. But despite its capriciousness, and for those prepared to come to grips with it, it was very profitable breeding and fattening country.

Passing through a gap between two tree-capped ridges Wyeera homestead suddenly appeared almost directly below them and, banking steeply, Saxon soon had them approaching the red dirt landing strip which had been cleared from the surrounding scrub. As they landed the buildings were promptly lost to sight behind intervening banks of trees, but before the aircraft had rolled to a halt and they had un-buckled their seatbelts a large red Range-Rover had made its appearance from the direction of the home-stead, a young man of some twenty-odd years at the wheel who proved to be Saxon's senior jackaroo.

The house itself, when it finally returned to view after their half-mile drive, was large and comfortable-looking rather than elaborate, the verandah rails and supports almost submerged beneath flowering creepers, a screened structure running the length of the twin-hipped roof.

'What's that?' Debra asked of Eleanor in a low voice, indicating the decking with a frown.

'Oh, that used to be our sleep-out for those un-bearably hot summer nights, in the days before air-conditioning,' the older woman smiled. 'Prue still likes to use it as such sometimes when she's staying with us, and it's very pleasant sitting up there on a summer's evening. If there's any breeze coming off the plains at all you'll catch it up there.'

'Mmm, I imagine you would,' she conceded, intrigued with the innovation. 'And with the screen to keep all the insects away ...'

'You don't care for insects, Miss Armitage?' The quietly spoken but irritatingly mocking enquiry came from Saxon as he half turned in the front seat to eye her over his shoulder.

'Not when they propose sharing my meals, drinks, or my bed, Mr McAllister, no, I don't particularly care for them,' she returned drily.

'Nor do I, dear, they can be so terribly annoying,' inserted Eleanor, stepping into the breech, as she had done on a number of occasions since the previous Saturday. Even though, for the most part, her stepson seemed reluctant to involve her in any of his clashes with their newest employee, sometimes it was unavoidable.

Saxon merely twisted his lips wryly at the hasty defence and, as the vehicle came to a stop before the central steps leading into the homestead, alighted and opened the rear door so the others could follow suit.

'It's good to be home,' Eleanor sighed contentedly and, as the two girls came to stand beside her, continued, 'Let's go in and have some tea, shall we? I'm sure Sherry will have a pot ready for us.'

Sherry turned out to be Mrs Sherrington, the housekeeper, a white-haired, trim woman of much the same age as Eleanor and who also had been widowed for some years. As far as Debra could make out, she and her husband had come to Wyeera only a short time after Saxon's father had remarried, and had been a permanent and well respected resident ever since.

In the end it was only Eleanor and Debra who enjoyed the welcome brew on the shaded verandah, Prue having decided to accompany the housekeeper back to the kitchen for her own special treat, and Saxon offering his excuses and saying he wanted to catch up on what had been happening on the property during his absence.

Their cups filled, Eleanor leant back in her padded chair and eyed her companion with a faintly anxious furrowing of her brow. 'I'm sorry Saxon has developed this penchant of his for—er—baiting you, Debra. I do hope it's not going to spoil your time here on Wyeera for you.'

Debra would have been more inclined to call her stepson's behaviour out-and-out harassment, but as she didn't want to put even deeper creases in the kindhearted woman's forehead she made light of it with a laugh and a casual hunching of her shoulders.

'No, of course it won't, I don't let it worry me enough to do that,' she lied glibly. 'I guess it's only natural that he's still somewhat suspicious of my motives in asking you for the position, but I expect that will fade in time,' adding a silently grimaced, 'Joke!' for her own benefit.

'I thought he would have been over it by now,' Eleanor mused thoughtfully. 'Although I suppose my giving you that advance on your wages without telling him didn't seem to help matters, did it? Goodness knows why, but he just refused to believe the idea hadn't been yours.'

'I know,' Debra gulped, recalling Saxon's absolutely arctic fury when he had discovered what his stepmother had done. Of course, she had already surmised what would happen—one of the reasons she had tried to dissuade Eleanor from making the advance—but the other woman had insisted once she had been informed—by her stepson, not Debra —of the events which had taken place after his escorting her home that Saturday night.

In fact, all in all it hadn't been a particularly promising first four days as far as Debra was concerned. Saxon McAllister had shown not even the slightest inkling that he was beginning to revise his opinion of her, and if it hadn't been for Eleanor and Prue's presence on Monday night at the Show she was certain the evening would have been purgatory from start to finish. As it was, he had still subtly managed to make her feel uncomfortable for accompanying them and she had been extremely thankful when they had finally returned to the hotel.

'Ah, well, I suppose all we can do is wait for his good sense to prevail once he gets to know you better,' Eleanor went on with an encouraging smile. 'As soon as he sees how well you fit in he'll change his ideas, I'm sure.'

Debra returned her smile noncommittally. It was very nice of Eleanor to be so confident she *would* fit in, but not even a round peg could slip into a round hole if someone was continually attempting to hammer it out again! She decided to tactfully change the subject.

'When will I actually be starting work, Eleanor? Tomorrow?' she asked.

A rueful smile crossed the other woman's features. 'To tell the truth, I haven't really given it a thought. Hasn't Saxon mentioned anything to you about it?'

'Not yet.'

'Then I expect he will at dinner this evening. We'll leave any decision till then, shall we?'

'If you like.' Debra was agreeable. Eleanor might have done the hiring, but as Saxon had so rightly implied, he was obviously the one in control on the property.

After that they talked desultorily on a variety of topics until they had finished their tea and then Eleanor had shown the younger girl to her room so that she might settle in before dinner as it was already well into the afternoon.

It was a lovely room, Debra noted pleasurably, once Eleanor had departed and she had an opportunity to look at it properly. Rectangular rather than square, it was tastefully furnished in tones of cream and willow green, the ruffled curtains at the windows of the same material as the flounced bedspread, the highly polished parquetry floor giving off a mirror shine. If she'd known she could exchange her depressing bed-sitter for a room like this, she smiled to herself wryly, she might have thought of looking in the country papers for work long before now. But until she had met the McAllisters it just hadn't occurred to her.

A half hour was all the time she needed to see her cases unpacked and her clothes neatly put away in wardrobe and dresser, and wondering what to do with herself from then until dinner, she was on the point of going for a walk when a knock on her door announced Prue's arrival.

'Grandma's having a rest, so she sent me along to see if you'd like me to show you around.' Her head tilted enquiringly. 'Would you?'

'Yes, very much,' Debra smiled down into the animated little face watching her so expectantly. 'As a matter of fact, I was just thinking of going exploring when you arrived. It will be much better to have someone with me who knows where everything is.'

'That's what Grandma said,' Prue confided as they began walking down the hall. 'What would you like to see first?'

'I don't mind, it's all new to me,' admitted Debra wryly.

'You mean, you've never been on a cattle station before . . . *ever*?'

'No, never. I haven't met anyone who owned one before.'

'I've been to lots,' her young guide divulged proudly. 'Grandma and Saxon often take me when they go visiting.'

'You've stayed on Wyeera quite a few times, then, I gather,' deduced Debra with a grin as they made their way down the front steps and into the garden.

'Oh, yes, Mummy and Daddy often have to go away on trips.' Prue stopped when they came to a flight of steps at the side of the house, turning to ask, 'Do you want to see the sleep-out?' and promptly added the warning, 'It'll still be very hot up there.'

Debra shrugged fatalistically. 'I don't mind, if you don't.'

'Come on, then!' Prue was halfway to the first landing before she had finished speaking, taking the steps two at a time, while Debra followed at a more natural speed.

She found it was unexpectedly high by the time she reached the top, and as her companion had foretold, still scorchingly hot with the sun's rays being reflected back from the silver-glossed decking so that one collected the heat both coming and going. Even worse than that she soon discovered, however, was the glare, and she immediately headed for the surrounding railings in an effort to avoid it by looking out over the far-reaching countryside. The view so gained more than made up for any discomfort, she decided, and while she allowed her gaze to roam over it unhindered, Prue knowledgeably pointed out the various landmarks for her.

A quick check of the decoratively grouped tubs and pots filled with gaily flowering cacti, and the banana loungers and chairs beneath a striped awning, were all she could manage afterwards before suggesting they adjourn to the ground once more. Her shirt already clinging to her back and clustered drops of perspiration had long since made their appearance at her temples.

'What did you think of it?' asked Prue brightly when they were back in the garden. 'Did you like it?'

Debra swept her long hair back from her face and laughed ruefully. 'I think I'd probably prefer it at night.'

'Well, maybe you'd like Grandma's water house better,' Prue now offered, shrugging her shoulders lightly and seemingly unaffected by the heat herself.

'Water house?' queried Debra.

'Mmm, you'll see. It's this way.'

The water house, as Prue had called it, was in actual fact a shade or bush house made of bark over a wire frame with water trickling continuously down the walls to create the humid atmosphere the outback didn't possess for the most dazzling display of orchids and tropical flowers Debra had ever seen.

'Oh, aren't they beautiful!' she exclaimed as she closed the door behind them, and feeling herself immediately assailed by a steamy heat this time. 'Did Eleanor grow them all herself?'

'Yes, she's the President of the Garden Club in town,' Prue nodded. 'Orchids are her favourites.'

'They'd be mine too if I could grow them like this,' vowed Debra as she bent to inspect an enormous cluster of perfect gold specimens.

Prue stopped beside a pot overflowing with arching stems lined with three-inch flowers of the deepest cerise. 'I like the Cooktown Orchid best. It's Queensland's floral emblem, you know.'

'Yes, and it's really lovely, isn't it?' Debra sighed and glanced about her again. 'Although, to be honest, I'd be hard pressed to say which I thought was the most beautiful, they're all so gorgeous. This one, for instance,' pointing to another pot, 'you could almost mistake its flowers for pansies.'

'I think that's what it's called ... a Pansy Orchid.'

'That seems appropriate, it's a very close likeness.' Then, after moving on a few steps, 'Do you know what any of these others are called?'

A wrinkling of her nose and Prue shook her head.

'Not really. Grandma's told me lots of their names, but I forget most of them. Oh, I remember this one, though, because it looks like its name,' she explained, rushing ahead to a mahogany, white and gold variety. 'It's a Slipper Orchid.'

Debra stooped to survey it more closely and found her attention riveted to the blooms behind it. Almost nine inches wide, their brilliant orange petals overlapping, they exuded an unbelievably lovely perfume.

'You don't happen to remember *their* name, I suppose?' she just had to ask.

'Epiphyllum ... Orchid Cactus,' supplied a male voice from the doorway, and had her spinning round to face its owner with her instincts immediately on the defensive.

'Thank you,' she acknowledged the information tautly, but when he showed no sign of either moving or speaking again, was forced into questioning, 'Did you—um—want me for something?'

Saxon flexed one shoulder negligently, his thumbs hooking into the leather belt of the fawn drills he had changed into since she had seen him last. 'I just thought you might have been interested to see the office,' he drawled. 'But of course, if you haven't the time ...'

The sentence was allowed to fade away, but the insinuation couldn't have been plainer to Debra. She was there to work, not to act like a guest!

'Naturally I have the time, Mr McAllister,' she answered quietly, a little selfconsciously. 'It's just that when Prue asked if I'd like her to show me around, I didn't realise ...'

'That you might be expected to actually do some work once in a while?' he interrupted ironically.

'No, that isn't what I meant at all!' she protested resentfully. And to the child still waiting beside her, 'Thank you for what you've shown me so far, Prue. Perhaps we can finish our tour another day, okay?'

'Sure,' Prue acquiesced easily as they began walking towards the door. 'Maybe we can do it on Saturday or Sunday.'

'It's a date.'

'Provided, of course, Debra's not working on the weekend,' Saxon reminded his niece drily as she passed him on her way out.

'Not both days she won't have to, will she?' Prue promptly turned to entreat.

He smiled down at her tolerantly. 'We'll see, little one, but there's a tremendous amount of paper work which has been mounting up while we've been away.'

'Just a couple of hours,' she wheedled, undaunted.

'Maybe on Sunday,' was as far as he would relent, but Prue seemed satisfied with the result, for she threw her arms around him in a brief hug and then, with a cheery, 'I'll see you,' for both of them, she was off and running back to the house.

As soon as she had gone the smile disappeared from Saxon's face and his eyes flicked back to Debra. 'We work when there's work to be done here, not according to whatever day of the week it happens to be,' he advised shortly. 'Just because the calendar says it's Saturday or Sunday it doesn't mean we can forget about the livestock for two days.'

'I didn't suppose it did,' she defended herself

swiftly. 'I just thought that, working in the office ...'

'You'd have a nice easy job with a lot of spare time on your hands?'

'No!' she flared, her violet eyes darkening dramatically. 'I just hadn't expected my hours to be so closely aligned with yours, that's all!'

'Then there wouldn't be much point in my employing a secretary if she wasn't available when I wanted her, would there?' he retorted sarcastically.

Debra inhaled a deep breath but refrained from answering. No matter what she said he would manage to find fault with it somehow, and she moved out into the sunshine again with her chin edging higher in mute rebellion. Saxon closed the door of the shade house and caught up with her as she stormed across the lawn towards the homestead. From the corner of her eye she could see his shapely mouth beginning to to curve humorously, and the thought that he found the situation amusing was infuriating.

'What's the rush?' he mocked.

The hunching of her slender shoulders might have given the appearance of indifference, but she still couldn't keep the snap out of her voice as she gibed, 'I wouldn't like to be accused of taking my time in order to avoid doing some work!'

'Did anyone say they were expecting you to *do* any work today?'

'Not in so many words, but ...'

'Then I suggest you don't put two and two together and make five, Miss Armitage.' The advice was goadingly given. 'Believe me, I'll let you know plainly enough when I want you to work.'

'Yes, Mr McAllister,' she acknowledged with doubtful submissiveness, and had the pleasure of seeing some of the glittering amusement in his eyes being replaced by suspicion.

The office was situated at the back of the house, overlooking the horse paddock and the countryside beyond. It was quite a large, though functional room, the furniture typical of a business area, the equipment modern in design, and the walls adorned with certificates and ribbons as well as pictures of Wyeera's prizewinning Brahman stud cattle.

Briefly, Saxon began explaining her duties and where everything was kept, but one piece of equipment, to which her eyes strayed apprehensively every now and then, he didn't mention at all. Deliberately, she suspected. Located on a table of its own, it looked something like a typewriter, except that it had a screen attached which rather resembled a small T.V. set. So far, what he had detailed didn't appear likely to cause her too many worries—the work would definitely be different from what she had been used to, but it certainly wasn't insurmountable. That machine, however, could put everything into an entirely different perspective, she surmised, and she continued to eye it askance.

'And this, of course,' at long last he got around to indicating the device, and she didn't know whether to feel glad or sorry, 'is our computer. Or, more correctly, micro-computer. It's invaluable for keeping our stud records and accounts up to date.'

'I see.' Debra swallowed heavily, her worst imaginings confirmed. 'And who—er—uses the computer?'

'You or I, naturally! Noreen, your predecessor, had more or less full charge of it.'

Lucky Noreen! she grimaced sardonically. Obviously, that girl had known how to use the damned thing! Up until now she had only seen them in shop windows, and even then she hadn't paid much attention. Now she was wishing she had!

'I presume you can operate a computer? Eleanor did tell you that was an essential part of your duties?' Saxon's voice broke in on her despondent musings brusquely, his eyes narrowing as a betraying flush of colour crept into her smooth cheeks and her violet gaze dropped a few inches.

'N-no,' she whispered throatily, nervously.

With a stifled epithet he reefed open the stationary cupboard door, retrieved a manual with a photo of the machine on the front cover from within, and thumped it down on to the desk with barely controlled savagery.

'Then I recommend you learn to operate one very quickly, sweetheart, because come Monday you'll be expected to extract information from those records and forward it to the printers for inclusion in our forthcoming sales brochure. And I don't want any foul-ups, understand?' he rapped out grimly.

Debra nodded rapidly, the tip of her tongue sweeping across lips which had suddenly become dry. 'May I take this to my room to study it?' she asked shakily, picking up the book.

'You'd do better to study it in here, in conjunction with the machine,' curtly.

'I suppose so,' she conceded in a troubled voice.

'I'll leave you to it, then.' He started for the doorway, a lithe swing to his stride. 'Take heart, they reckon even a child can master them with only a reasonable amount of practice.'

The slightly patronising gibe sliced through her anxiety with a biting thrust and had her muttering acidly after his retreating figure, 'Which, no doubt, accounts for *your* being able to use it!'

His about-face was so swiftly executed that Debra couldn't believe her eyes. She hadn't meant him to hear her caustic remark!

'Would you care to repeat that?' he demanded stonily as he stalked back into the room.

As quickly as it had arisen her burst of rebellion now vanished and, backing away, she shook her head uneasily. 'I—I'm sorry,' she offered contritely, her pulse racing at his nearness when he leant one hand on the filing cabinet behind her and bent towards her.

For an interminable time he didn't speak as his gaze locked with her wide and wary one, and then, when he did, it was in a totally unanticipated tone, almost as if he had completely changed what he intended to say.

'Sweetheart, a challenge is one thing, but to tempt Providence is a different matter entirely.' One long forefinger slowly traced the line of her jaw from ear to chin with demoralising effect. 'So how about you concentrate on that book and forget about trying to provoke me, hmm?'

Debra wished she could move away. She felt horribly vulnerable with him standing so close. But with the cabinet behind her and a desk by her side there was nowhere to go.

'Well, you shouldn't have goaded me first,' she reproached, albeit a little breathlessly, but feeling she had to assert herself somehow.

His white teeth gleamed in a lazy smile. 'If you don't like the conditions, Miss Armitage, you can always resign,' he drawled.

And give him such an easy victory? He had to be kidding! But at least his suggestion gave her the courage to push past him with assumed nonchalance, her whole demeanour one of amused disdain.

'Oh, no, I'm not that easily routed, Mr McAllister! In fact, from what I've seen so far, I think the conditions here will suit me admirably—with one or two exceptions, of course—but then no position is perfect in every respect, is it?' she smiled mockingly.

'And your's likely to become very much less so the longer you remain!' His retaliation was swift, his intention painfully obvious.

With a shrug she dismissed it as carelessly as possible. 'Perhaps.'

'Definitely!' he corrected adamantly, and took his departure with an unhurried arrogance.

By dinner time Debra felt she had become, if not proficient in their use, then at least familiar with some of the more basic commands and statements required to operate the computer. There were a few chapters she skipped, reserving them in her mind for later study, which detailed functions she guessed—hoped—wouldn't be of paramount importance at the moment, and preferring to take more time over those explaining the methods employed for the keeping of data records and inventory systems.

Even so, she would still have been the first to admit that there was a long, long way to go before she could claim any sort of competency, and almost as soon as their evening meal had been concluded she made her excuses in order that she might return to the office.

Eleanor apparently thought she intended to retire for the night. 'You're tired after our journey today, are you?' she asked in a kindly manner. 'I find flying makes me quite sleepy too.'

Unconsciously, Debra's gaze slid towards the man at the head of the table, met a pair of electrifying blue eyes which held a decided taunt, and abruptly reversed direction.

'Yes, well, I would like to be fresh to start work tomorrow,' she evaded, reluctant to reveal where she was going in case it reminded Saxon yet again of his stepmother's somewhat impetuous method of employing her.

'Oh, that's right, we were going to discuss when you should start at dinner, weren't we?'

'Don't worry about it, Eleanor, Miss Armitage and I have already settled that question,' her stepson interposed smoothly.

'*Miss* Armitage, Saxon?' She looked down the table with a frown. 'Surely you're both not intending to continue addressing each other so formally now that we're home?'

The blond streaks in his hair glinted brightly as he moved his head in a slight downward movement. 'Then if you prefer it ... Debra.' His expression became mocking as he made his acknowledgment.

'Saxon.' She promptly aped his sardonic bearing in return.

'That's much better,' applauded Eleanor with a pleased smile, apparently oblivious to the glimmering undercurrents—or perhaps purposely ignoring them. And to Debra, 'You run along, my dear, if you want to, and we'll see you in the morning, after you've had a good night's rest.'

Keeping up the pretence, Debra bade them goodnight and then made her way back to the office where she settled down again in front of the computer. Slowly the minutes, then the hours, ticked past and the longer she remained there the more frustrated she became. She was doing something wrong, that she knew, but what? Even the machine kept throwing the word up at her. Either that or 'How?' And try as she might she just couldn't find where she was making her mistakes.

It didn't help that she was getting tired either, or was close to tears at being foiled by a machine, but she was determined she wouldn't leave it until she'd had at least one success in programming and adding to an indexed file. Sighing with despair for the umpteenth time, she rubbed the tips of her fingers across her creased brow and prepared to start at the beginning of the chapter again. Maybe if she took it step by step right from the start she would discover where she was going wrong.

So busy concentrating was she that it wasn't until the video displayed yet another querying sign, at which she muttered some withering remarks, and heard someone make a faintly taunting sound of reproof behind her, that she realised she had company. And unwanted company at that!

'I only said you had to be able to operate the computer by Monday ... not tomorrow,' Saxon advised—but not without some evidence of amusement in his tone, she noted with a grimace—as he peered over her shoulder to see the printing on the screen more clearly. 'You do realise it's after twelve, I suppose?'

Refusing to turn and look at him, he was far too close for her to do that with any sort of composure, Debra kept her eyes riveted to the screen. 'Goodness, but it's amazing how time flies when you're having fun, isn't it?' she quipped through gritted teeth. She was surprised it was only after twelve, it felt more like after three!

'You're finding the instructions quite simple to follow, then? No problems?'

On top of her setbacks of the evening the mocking enquiry was just too much and unbidden tears flooded her eyes. 'No problems,' she denied huskily.

As if she needed it pointed out to her, Saxon indicated the video unit. 'The computer doesn't appear to agree with you.'

Debra clenched her hands in her lap, still trying to blink the betraying wetness from her dusky lashes. 'They're not infallible,' she murmured evasively.

'You don't think the operator could have something to do with it?'

It was the smile she could see reflected on the screen which finally forced her into facing him. It goaded insupportably! 'All right, all right!' she blazed. 'So I'm not having much success! Now I suppose you're going to make some gloating remark and say it's no more than I deserve!'

'No, I was going to ask if you needed help, if you must know.'

That stopped her dead in her tracks and she eyed him doubtfully, mistily. 'Are you offering any?' she queried tentatively.

'If you want it.' His lips curved upwards wryly.

She nodded quickly, before he had a chance to remember he'd planned to make things harder for her, not easier. 'I certainly seem to need something,' she confessed a little selfconsciously.

Saxon pulled a chair closer and straddled it. 'Mmm, they can be confusing if you're not sure of what you're doing,' he smiled lazily.

Debra averted her gaze in confusion. Why he was deigning to be helpful she had no idea, but the sudden change in his manner was having a calamitous effect upon her senses. When he looked at her like that her defences were about as substantial as a wet tissue!

'Now, how about you showing me where you're getting this problem you're supposedly not having?'

His drily voiced suggestion broke in on her musings and brought her attention back to her immediate difficulties with a start.

'Oh—er—it's somewhere in here, I think,' she stammered, and pointed to the troublesome section outlined in the manual. 'I can get so far and then it keeps tossing up a "What?" or a "How?" at me.'

'Well, a "What?" means it doesn't understand what you want it to do, whereas a "How?" means it understands what you want but that you haven't explained how you want it done. So let's take it from the beginning and see if we can find where you're going wrong, hmm?'

All too willing to agree, Debra surreptitiously brushed the back of her hand across her eyes in order to dispose of the last of her involuntary tears, and started feeding the programme into the machine for yet another time. Line by line they went through it together and finally, after repeating the whole exercise two or three times, she was able to manage it on her own.

'You really mean that a missed full stop or a misplaced semi-colon can throw the whole programme out?' she asked slightly incredulously after her last successful run-through.

Saxon didn't immediately reply as his eyes ranged from her to the book and back again, ironically. 'Somehow I get the feeling you haven't read everything in that book that you should have done.'

'Well, it was so thick,' she grimaced excusingly, not looking at him. She was too conscious of the heavily muscled and tanned forearms resting on the back of the chair beside her as it was. 'I—I tried to pick out those chapters I thought would be most appropriate for your type of records.'

'And thereby missed some of the most fundamental and important instructions.'

There was nothing to be gained by denying it and Debra didn't even attempt to. Instead she shot him a brief look of enquiry. 'Why *did* you help me, anyway? You said you were going to make things as difficult as possible for me.'

'Except that, in this particular instance, I considered my peace of mind to be more convenient than your discomfort,' he divulged drily.

'I don't follow you.'

Saxon rose lithely to his feet but continued resting his hands on the back of the chair as he leant towards her, his expression sardonic. 'Let loose among those records while still incompetent there was no telling what havoc you may have wrought, and on thinking the matter over I found I wasn't prepared to take the chance.'

'I see,' she murmured quietly, a little disappointedly. She had hoped he was beginning to relent in his attitude.

Perhaps some regret was evident in her tone, for now his well shaped brows lifted to their more familiar mocking slant and he taunted, 'You surely hadn't persuaded yourself I'd succumb beneath the avalanche of those crocodile tears of yours?'

She should have known he would think they had only been put on for his benefit! But rather than let him know they hadn't been feigned, she merely shrugged indifferently. 'It was worth a try,' she perjured herself with brittle lightness.

'But not quite good enough to take *me* in, sweetheart!' he retorted, an unmistakable note of contempt entering his voice. 'You forget, I know just what a hard-headed, conniving little piece you really are!'

Somehow Debra managed to smother her furious indignation beneath a fragile veneer of unconcern. 'Then I shall just have to find some other way to spike your guns, shan't I?' she proposed chaffingly. 'Who knows what worthwhile method for getting under your guard a coldly calculating little brain like the one you keep crediting me with is capable of devising. I notice you're not exactly averse to changing your attitude when it happens to suit *your* purpose.'

'Meaning?' ominously.

She swallowed hard but refused to be outstared. 'This evening ... your precious records,' she reminded him ironically. 'Perhaps if I ...'

Before she even had a chance to finish what she was saying her head was abruptly snapped back as a handful of her long hair was wrapped around strong fingers and pulled tight.

'Don't you try threatening me, you little vixen, or you'll wish you'd never heard of a McAllister, let alone met one!' he lowered his head to grate implacably.

Actually, a threat had been the furthest thing from her mind, and for a moment she could only stare up at him in shaken surprise. Then, as the pain from her captive hair began to register, her eyes darkened with a smouldering resentment.

'You seem to do it often enough!' she glared accusingly, and futilely attempting to break his hold. 'So why can't I?'

'Because I happen to be the injured party!'

With her hair feeling as if half of it was being dragged out by its roots, Debra wasn't quite sure how he could make that statement. 'That's a laugh!' she jeered insolently. 'I didn't think it was possible to injure case-hardened steel!'

His cold blue eyes roamed over her critically, insultingly. 'And *I* didn't think it was possible for anyone to *look* so desirable, and yet *be* such an un-desirable!' he derided harshly as he released her.

'Then you obviously haven't taken a good look at yourself in the mirror of late!' she hurled back sarcastically, her breath coming in shuddering gasps, her eyes watering. Her scalp was stinging fiercely, but she wouldn't give him the satisfaction of seeing her massage it with him present.

Recovering his equanimity, Saxon flexed solid shoulders imperturbably. 'You can always leave.'

'I'll see you in hell first!' she gibed.

He laughed, a short, scornful sound. 'Don't count on it!' was his parting advice as he strode from the room.

CHAPTER FOUR

DURING the next three days Debra worked harder than she had probably ever done before, and at the same time had been criticised—unfairly on most occasions, she believed—more often than ever before as well. Evidently Saxon was determined to be the hardest taskmaster imaginable, with the result that she hadn't seemed to have a minute to herself since arriving on the property. Oh, he'd allowed her a couple of hours off during Sunday afternoon—only because Prue had managed to cajole them out of him previously, she was positive—but for the rest of the time there had hardly been space for her to draw breath, and by Monday morning she was looking forward to the break from his ever watchful scrutiny, and needling, while she drove Prue to school in Acacia Crossing.

'Are you coming with us today, Grandma?' Prue asked as she was preparing to leave the table after breakfast.

'No, dear, not today,' Eleanor smiled, and shook her head. 'I think I'd better take the chance to look to my orchids while I have the time. I've hardly been near them since we came home.'

Prue accepted this in her stride and looked across the table, another query on her lips. 'Will you be long, Debra?'

Sensing her anxiety to be on her way Debra

73

glanced at her watch. 'But it's only just after seven!' she exlaimed.

'It used to take Noreen almost two hours,' Prue shrugged philosophically.

And Noreen had probably been an experienced driver! Debra swallowed her mouthful of toast, had a quick drink of tea, and jumped to her feet.

'Well, you collect whatever you need, then, and ... if you'll excuse me,' her glance encompassed both Eleanor and Saxon who were still seated at the table, 'we'll be off.'

'Do you know which vehicle to take?' Saxon's voice came drawling after her as she neared the doorway.

She swung about, her expression wary, and saw him also rising to his feet. 'I thought Prue would probably know,' she said.

'And you'd have no trouble driving whichever one she chose?'

Now was no time to show lack of confidence! 'I don't expect so.' She held his gaze determinedly as he approached.

He didn't appear particularly convinced, but at least he didn't comment either, merely saying to his stepmother, 'I'll be off too, Eleanor. I'll see you later.'

'Yes, dear,' she acknowledged placidly. And to Debra, 'Have a good trip, but watch out for those road-trains, won't you?'

'I will,' Debra promised, even as her thoughts turned apprehensive. How many of those powerful prime movers hauling three or four double-decker stock trailers behind them was she likely to meet on the road? Not too many she hoped!

Saxon retrieved his hat from the hallstand as he accompanied her out on to the verandah, clamping it down on his head in businesslike fashion. 'Normally, you'd take the station wagon, but there's some rolls of wire to be picked up in town this morning, so it had better be the ute. I'll show you where it's kept,' he offered casually.

'There's really no need for you to bother. Prue showed me yesterday.'

'It's no bother, that's where I'm headed too.'

Prue met them at the five-bay garage where she quickly ascertained which vehicle they were travelling in and clambered inside together with her school case. Debra checked to see the keys were in the ignition and prepared to follow suit, frowning when Saxon opened the passenger door again and slid on to the bench alongside his niece.

'Are we—er—going past where you want to go——' she enquired hesitantly.

'No, straight to it,' he advised levelly before turning to send her a deeply sardonic glance. 'You didn't really think I'd trust you to drive Prue into town on your own without first checking to see how competent a driver you were, did you?'

'I guess not,' she was forced into acceding, although she really hadn't thought about it before, and right at the moment she had other things on her mind. She was trying to discover where everything was located.

'What are you used to, a floor or column change?'

Momentarily she stopped searching in order to look at him blankly. 'I beg your pardon?'

'The gears, sweetheart,' he elucidated drily, tapping the appropriate lever. 'On the floor, or on the steering column?'

'Oh!' She flushed embarrassedly. 'On the steering column, the same as this.'

'That's something, I suppose,' he commented with a look of long-suffering.

Debra ignored him as best she could and prayed she wouldn't make a mistake as she switched the engine on and, after only two attempts, found reverse. Nonetheless, their passage out of the garage wasn't exactly sedate and she had, perforce, to slam on the brakes suddenly when she saw the homestead fence rushing to meet them. Prue giggled enjoyably as they all perked backwards on the seat, but Saxon didn't look anywhere near as amused.

'I didn't ask to see it, but I presume you *do* have a licence?' he queried stonily.

'Of course!' Luckily her forward progress was proving somewhat smoother. 'I'm not used to this model car, that's all!'

'Well, try and get used to it before we hit the highway, hmm? I'm not in the mood for a harrowing experience right now.'

'In that case, why don't you just close your eyes and let *me* do the driving?' she suggested bittersweetly.

To her utter amazement he took her at her word, easing further down on to the seat and tipping his hat forward over his eyes. 'Okay, it's all yours,' he yielded with surprising docility—although apparently not quite so complacently that he was able to resist nudging Prue and recommending in a stage whisper, 'You'd better ask if she checked whether we've got enough fuel to get us to town, otherwise we could spend most of the day stranded beside the road.'

Prue laughed, thinking it was a game, but Debra knew differently and her gaze flicked hastily down to the gauge. A second later she expelled a small sigh of relief. She would never have heard the end of it if they'd run out of gas on the way! Now it was she who nudged Prue on the arm.

'You can tell your uncle to relax,' she charged wryly. 'I wouldn't dream of inconveniencing him to such an extent.'

'Debra says....,' Prue began her relay with a grin.

'I heard,' the man beside her drawled lazily.

Chancing a covert sideways glance, Debra could just make out the corner of his firmly moulded mouth as it inclined upwards in whimsical recognition of her light gibe and she looked away again swiftly, her stomach somersaulting crazily. He would be easier to dislike if he wasn't so damned attractive, she decided ruefully.

Considering the highway wasn't paved for the most part, it was still relatively comfortable driving. Some sections were worse than others, of course, but on the whole Debra found the trip less of an ordeal than she had anticipated. The ute was fortunately possessed of a smooth manoeuvrability and after the first thirty-odd miles she found she could relax as she had suggested their unexpected passenger do.

Once it became apparent her uncle didn't intend taking part in their conversation Prue kept up a steady stream of chatter which at times was quite informative from Debra's point of view when it concerned the surrounding district or personages in the area, so that by the time the signposts denoted they were approaching Acacia Crossing she was pleasantly surprised that the journey hadn't taken longer.

'I thought you said it was a two-hour trip,' she looked down at Prue quizzically. 'It's only taken us an hour and a half.'

'Mmm, but Noreen didn't used to get a move on like you did, she was always looking out for people she knew so she could stop and talk. One time I was even half an hour late for school.'

'Well, that's certainly not going to happen today. You're almost an hour early.'

'That's good.' Prue gave her approval with a wide, pleased smile. 'Now I can have as long to play as some of the others.'

'Right you are, then,' Debra grinned in return, remembering her own desire to arrive early for just such a reason. 'Where is the school?'

They had just started to pass a collection of houses at the beginning of the main street and Prue pointed ahead of them quickly. 'The last building on the left, down the end,' she said.

Debra glanced about her with interest as they continued down the now bitumened road. It wasn't a particularly large town—there was only a small scattering of shops—with the hotel, stock and station agents and bank taking pride of place in the middle of the block. But as they came abreast of them Saxon suddenly eased upright and pushed his hat back into its rightful position, and making her wonder if, indeed, he had shut his eyes at all.

'You can let me out here,' he advised, motioning towards the middle one of the 'big three' as Debra had thought of them. 'After you've dropped Prue off, you can go round to Simpson's and collect that wire, then call back, okay?'

She shrugged equably. It didn't sound too difficult. But as she pulled to a stop and he prepared to alight, she waved one hand to indicate the rest of the buildings. 'Which one's Simpson's?' she queried wryly.

Saxon gained his feet and then had to stoop to look back into the cabin of the ute. 'It's round the back of the store,' gesturing diagonally across the street. 'Prue will show you from the school, you can see it from there.'

Scant minutes later she was halting again, this time to let Prue out.

'That's where you have to go,' she was informed, and had a large ramshackle old wooden building set some way behind the main street pointed out to her.

'I see it.' Her smile was appreciatively given. 'And I'll pick you up here this afternoon when school comes out.

'It doesn't matter if you're a bit late,' Prue put in hurriedly, her words sounding more like a hint than accommodation. 'You don't *have* to be here right on time. I can always wait at Jenny Dutton's house for you.'

'Is that what you used to do when Noreen collected you?'

'Most times. She wouldn't arrive until half past four, or even later.' Judging by her expression Noreen's tardiness *after* school hours wasn't condemned, at least not by Prue.

'Doesn't Mrs Dutton mind?' Debra was still a little doubtful, though.

Prue shook her head vigorously. 'No, she always says that once you've got eight of your own you never notice another one or two.'

'No, I guess maybe not,' Debra laughed. 'Well, as long as she doesn't mind ...' She was partway to relenting. 'I'll check with your uncle on the way home, all right?'

'Sure!' Evidently that had been the right comment to make, for the little face was now wreathed in smiles. 'Saxon always lets me stay on for a while.' Then as a carrot-haired moppet called to her from the schoolhouse steps she proffered a rushed, ' 'Bye, Debra, I'll see you this afternoon,' and was hurrying across the grass towards her friend.

Simpson's, Debra soon discovered after driving into one of the many loading docks, was a produce store which catered mainly for property owners and sold a variety of goods and implements as diverse as heavy machinery and flea powder. The air was redolent of chaff, mixed feeds, molasses, and a number of other equally strong but indistinguishable aromas, and she sniffed experimentally as she made her way past piled sacks of unknown substances to a glass-partitioned office where a grey-haired man looked up enquiringly on noting her presence.

One glance at the vehicle she was using, however,

immediately produced a smiled, 'I know the ute, but not the face.'

'Debra Armitage,' she supplied with a laugh. 'I'm the new secretary at Wyeera.'

'Ah, taken young Noreen's place, have you? I'm Pat Beasley.' He came out of the office, a mountain of a man and as strong as an ox by the look of him, his bushy brows lifting. 'You've come for Mac's wire, I suppose?'

Mac? Oh, McAllister! It took a little time to register. 'Yes, please,' she nodded.

'Right you are, lass, we'll have it loaded for you in two shakes.'

And so it was. The huge rolls being dropped into the back of the ute as if they had weighed no more than a few pounds each, but managing to make the vehicle rock heavily each time one of them landed all the same.

On the receiving end of a cheery wave Debra was soon back behind the wheel again and heading down the street to the stock and station agents where she reverse angle parked and somewhat hesitantly entered the office. She was uncertain as to whether Saxon had meant for her to actually call for him or just to wait outside.

As she walked in she could see a young girl bending over some boxes in one corner of the reception area, but before she could speak to her a male voice sounded from one of the two inner offices.

'Come on through!' it bade. 'We're almost finished.'

Only moving forward enough so she could poke

her head around the doorway, Debra smiled deprecatorily at the two men inside. 'I—it's only me.' Her glance slid to Saxon, who had just risen to his feet. 'Maybe I'd better wait for you in the ute.'

Her wrist was caught and held in a firm grip even as she took her first step backwards. 'Now that you're here it might be an idea if you met Mike. You'll probably be talking to him on the phone often enough during the next few weeks,' Saxon declared, drawing her inexorably into the room. 'Simmonds' Primary are the major agents who'll be handling the auction.'

Debra nodded her understanding, feeling rather like a recalcitrant child with her wrist still captive, and thankful when Saxon was compelled to release it during her ensuing introduction to Mike Allworth.

'And how are you liking it so far at Wyeera?' she was asked after they had exchanged greetings. 'Noreen always used to say it was one of the easiest jobs she'd ever had.'

It was almost all Debra could do to stop pulling a sardonic grimace. No doubt Noreen had received completely different treatment from what she was getting too!

'Well, it's certainly different from the last job I had,' she skirted giving a direct answer. 'But I'm sure I'll get the better of it in time.' This last for the enlightenment of her employer.

'Mmm, she's nothing if not a quick worker,' inserted Saxon ironically, and she knew he was referring to the manner in which she had gained employment and not her ability.

'Just what you need with the sales coming up,

Mac.' The other man accepted his statement at face value.

'As long as she's not so fast that she gets ahead of me,' he drawled wryly.

Mike laughed and winked at Debra. 'You keep him on his toes, love,' he exhorted. 'I've noticed the paper work's been a bit on the slow side coming out of Wyeera for the last few months.'

'Well, I'll certainly do my best to keep him up to the mark,' she replied to his suggestion in joking kind, her wide-spaced eyes openly provoking as they connected with Saxon's azure gaze. 'But if someone's just naturally slow to work things out ...' The sentence was allowed to trail away insinuatingly, lugubriously.

This time it was the nape of her neck which felt the warmth of Saxon's hand as she was urged towards the door in front of him. 'On your way!' he ordered, but with more dryness than annoyance in his tone, she noted with relief. 'Before either of you can cast any more aspersions.' And over his shoulder. 'We'll get moving now, Mike.'

'Okay, Mac. I'll be in touch. With you too, Debra.'

She turned her head back as much as the hand on her neck would permit. 'I'll look forward to it,' she smiled sincerely.

Once outside she slid out from under the disconcerting touch as rapidly as possible, and in an effort to disguise the nervous movement turned to ask, 'Do you want to drive?'

Saxon shrugged indifferently. 'No, you can.'

'Are there any other stops you want to make before we leave town?' she thought it best to enquire as she fastened her seatbelt a few minutes later.

'Just the Post Office. It's further down on this side.'

On looking up to acknowledge the information Debra found him surveying her with an indolent thoroughness and her gaze wavered confusedly. 'You sure made the most of your opportunity back there, didn't you?' he observed drily.

'So did you,' she half smiled, still very wary of his mood. 'But then I've never been one to look a gift horse in the mouth.'

Even before the words were completely out she knew she couldn't have chosen a worse quote to use, and his tersely clipped, 'So I've noticed!' only served to accentuate her unthinking mistake.

Damn! For a while that had been just about the closest they'd come to anything even approaching amity, and now, through a careless slip of the tongue, she had put them right back where they started. Despondently, she turned the ignition key and put the car into gear.

For most of their journey home Saxon was occupied with the mail he had collected. There seemed mountains of it to Debra—periodicals and newspapers, catalogues and brochures, and an apparently unending supply of letters. Whether this was the normal amount of mail they received, or had been brought about owing to the forthcoming sale, she didn't know, but she did take a wry guess and surmise that there would be even more work ahead of her when they reached Wyeera.

So busy had she been in casting rapid glances over the mound of assorted paper between them, however, that she didn't realise they had come upon one of the worst sections of the road until they hit the first pothole with a shuddering thump, together with quite a number of following ones before the half-mile horror stretch was left safely behind them.

'Did you manage to get them all?' Saxon took time out from the letter he was perusing to spare her a heavily sarcastic glance as they jolted their way over the last gouged cavity.

'I think so,' she retorted facetiously. 'I wouldn't want a whole morning to go past without giving you the chance to find fault with at least *something* I'd done.'

'You make the errors, sweetheart. I just point them out to you.'

'And so politely too!' she gibed. 'With all the finesse and consideration of an attacking shark!'

'You knew it wouldn't be consideration you'd be receiving from me when you insisted on taking the position, so why the complaints now? Regretting your decision at last, are you?' he taunted.

'Not my decision, your pigheadedness!' Her retaliation came promptly, recklessly. 'You need a secretary, especially at the moment, and I need the job. You'd be in a worse position if you didn't have anyone at all, and I can't see why you refuse to admit that we can both benefit from the arrangement.'

'Then it will be my pleasure to inform you why!' The abrupt corrosiveness in his tone sent shivers down her spine. 'Firstly, because nothing alters the facts! You weren't qualified for the position, and I still take strong exception to the manner in which you came by it. Secondly, and before you get carried away with thinking you're indispensable, I would just like to make it clear that since you've been here you have partially filled a gap ... nothing more! Although the work for which you've been trained may be satisfactory, your shorthand leaves a lot to be desired, you're still unreliable—to say the least—with the computer, and your driving ...' he shot her a look filled with stinging mockery, 'is tending to become erratic. Would you mind keeping your speed down a little until you know the road better?'

It was true her foot had been pressing down harder during his scornful diatribe, but it wasn't until she actually looked at the speedometer that Debra realised just how hard and, with a sharply indrawn breath, she eased it off again. Not that she didn't consider her foot had cause to become heavy. She felt that way all over now. Saxon's remarks had been fashioned to cause the most hurt and they had achieved their purpose extremely well!

'I s-still don't think you're being entirely f-fair,' she began, and was dismayed to hear an unmistakable tremor in her voice.

'I told you the night we met I didn't intend to be,' he countered roughly.

'So you did.' The dampness beginning to creep on to her lashes she blinked away furiously. She wasn't going to be accused of producing false tears again. 'Along with the threat to make my life hell, if I remember correctly.'

'And have I?'

'No!' she denied thickly, defiantly, although not altogether truthfully.

'Never say die, huh?' He read between the lines shrewdly.

'Not to you!'

His following smile was slow and confident. 'We'll see.'

Somehow his statement had an ominous ring to it and Debra couldn't help turning to look at him. In the sunlight her eyes were a deep shimmering violet, very beautiful, but very apprehensive. For a brief second their glances held, and then she had to turn back to the road.

'Sorry, sweetheart, it doesn't wash,' Saxon grated caustically.

'I beg your pardon?' Her forehead furrowed in bafflement.

'The wide-eyed, damsel in distress look!'

When her gaze flashed momentarily his way this time her expression of anxiety had been displaced by one of seething rebellion. 'I wouldn't waste my time even trying to appeal to your finer feelings, Saxon McAllister, because I sincerely doubt if you have any!' she disparaged vehemently.

'Not where you're concerned, at any rate!' he immediately returned with equal acrimony.

Debra bit at her lip as a dark wave of depression rolled inexorably over her. It all seemed so terribly one-sided, and her original counter-threat to make his life unbearable as well a tiny ineffectual voice crying in the wind. No matter what she said or did he immediately suspected her motives and, although he had gone to great pains to decry her performance so far, she still didn't consider her efforts to have been total failures. True, she had made some mistakes—

didn't everyone in a new job?—but nowhere near as many as he liked to imply, and certainly none of any magnitude.

Engrossed as she was in her own musings, Saxon needed to repeat his instruction for her to pull over when the driver of a car approaching from the opposite direction indicated his intention to do the same, his second command being issued in a far more forceful voice and accompanied by a sarcastic, 'Or is that asking too much of your capabilities?'

Deeming it best not to reply to such a taunting gibe, she merely shrugged and eased to a stop on the gravelled shoulder of the road and sat waiting as Saxon alighted and walked to the front of the ute, where he was shortly joined by the other driver. Not that she could hear anything but a muted murmur from their conversation, but Debra guessed them to be old friends by the manner of their expressions and easy demeanour, the stranger being of approximately the same age as her employer, his features clean-cut and pleasant.

A few minutes later both men walked towards her open window and she found herself staring into a pair of deeply appreciative brown eyes as Saxon introduced her to Paul Bartlett, the son of a neighbouring property owner.

'I was just discussing the details with Mac for our cricket match next Sunday,' he relayed. 'I suppose you'll be playing for Wyeera.'

'I—I don't know,' she half smiled after her eyes had moved involuntarily to Saxon and then back again when no help had been forthcoming. 'Do the women usually play?'

'The younger ones do when it's a charity match like this one. All proceeds from the day are for the local hospital, but there's a dozen bottles of champagne for the winners.' Resting his forearms on the edge of the window, he eyed her in mock interrogation. 'Have you ever played before?'

'A little,' she admitted with a laugh. At the orphanage it had always been a case of one in, all in.

'Then that settles it, she definitely plays for Wyeera,' Saxon broke in, grinning banteringly at his friend.

'Don't be too sure!' Paul's return look was just as chafing. 'Remember, the match is on our place this year and *I'm* the one who'll be making up the teams. You already have too many good batsmen as it is.'

'But not batswomen,' came the swift counter-change.

'The teams all consist of an equal number from both sexes,' Paul advised Debra in an aside before turning to retort, 'I don't know about that! One of your stockmen's wives made mincemeat of our bowling last time.'

'Ah, but neither Joy nor Kevin will be playing this year, they're away on leave at the moment.'

'I can't say I'm sorry,' joked Paul wryly. 'The pair of them scored far too many runs for my liking.'

'The bowling's not too fast, is it?' Debra inserted a little nervously after pondering his previous remark.

His eyes twinkled as he smiled down at her. 'No, we're very gallant where the ladies are concerned. The first time you're dismissed isn't counted and we bowl underarm. Unless, of course, you start slogging us all over the paddock, in which case we may be tempted to resort to stronger measures,' he grinned.

Pearl-white teeth gleamed in acknowledgment. 'And the men, do they get two chances as well?' she asked.

'Good lord, no! It's fair dinkum when one of us is at the crease.' He looked across at Saxon and started to laugh. 'A fight to the last ditch, you might say, eh, old son?'

'And especially if it's Noonameena and Wyeera who make the final,' was the dry reply.

Noonameena being the Bartletts' property, surmised Debra. 'From which, I gather, there's more than just two teams taking part?' she directed her question towards Paul.

'Mmm, although that more or less depends on how many people arrive. We can usually manage about four teams, though, but with considerably more than the accepted number of eleven a side, of course.'

Her arched brows lifted slightly in surprise. 'In that case, wouldn't it take all day just to play one game?'

He shook his head quickly and smiled. 'Not really. You see, we put a limit on the number of runs anyone's allowed to score, we only have single innings, and there's also a restriction on the number of balls bowled. Apart from that,' his dark brown eyes danced humorously, 'not many of our players are that good that they stay at the wicket for very long, anyway.'

'I'm not surprised if you have such large fielding sides.'

'Oh, we rarely have the whole team on the field at the one time,' he discounted. 'That's the men's province in the main, while the women see to the food and drinks, etcetera. The day's intended as a social get-together rather than sports event, so if you would rather sit and talk you can, but if you want to field you can do that also.'

'In other words, everyone does their own thing,' she laughed.

'Just about,' he agreed with an answering, and admiring, smile.

'Right—well, if there's nothing else you wanted to see me about, Paul, we'd better be on our way.' Saxon successfully put an end to their conversation and began moving around the front of the vehicle. 'Debra has a considerable amount of work to do before she collects Prue this afternoon.'

'Okay, Mac.' His friend reluctantly levered himself away from the ute. 'I'll see you both on Sunday, then?'

'Uh-huh,' Saxon concurred laconically.

With a last smile and a salute to the brim of his hat Paul took his leave and headed across the road while Saxon regained his seat, and then they were mobile again.

'Does everyone call you Mac?' Debra queried interestedly, thankful for the breeze that had begun blowing through the cabin again.

'Only my friends.'

Hiding a grimace, she concentrated on the road ahead. Another snub for Miss Armitage? she asked herself wryly. It was becoming a demoralising but, no doubt from his point of view, successful habit. With a sigh she recalled another matter she had to ask him about.

'Prue mentioned she sometimes stays in town to play with one of her friends after school. I said I would check with you whether it was all right for me to pick her up later in the afternoon,' she explained.

'It is, provided you keep a sharp eye out for kangaroos on the way home,' he allowed levelly. 'As the day gets cooler they like to feed alongside the road and they have the unnerving habit of waiting until you're right beside them and then deciding they want to cross over.'

'I'll be careful,' she vowed earnestly. The responsibility for someone else's child she was discovering to be quite a sobering one.

By now Saxon had returned his attention to the mail and Debra was happy to complete the remainder of the journey in silence—and even happier when, after driving the ute down to the store shed, she found he didn't plan to accompany her back to the office but simply handed the mail to her, along with the perfunctory question, 'You're clear on what information needs to be taken from the files?'

'Yes, thank you.'

Her answer was confident, and so was she, but when she was actually at the typewriter and starting to record all the necessary details from the computer, what she suddenly realised she hadn't envisaged was just how time-consuming the work would be. For every stud animal listed for the auction there was a tremendous amount of information which needed to be gathered.

First there was the name and Lot number of the animal itself, together with its calving date, registration number, colour, and tatoo number. Then she had to extract the names of the four preceding generations in the sire's line, but luckily, only three in the dam's. Even so, it still amounted to another twenty-two animals which had to be noted each time —along with all their triple-barrelled names and five or six-figured registration numbers, of course!

When lunchtime arrived she had just about managed to memorise the reference sire's pedigree, only to discover as she turned the page of notes Saxon had left with her that the following group had come from a different parent altogether and that she would need to repeat the exercise all over again.

The one redeeming feature of her morning was that only Eleanor joined her for the midday meal in the dining room, thereby giving her the opportunity to relax a little, as well as escape from what she could well imagine would be the undeserved, but no less scathing, comments of her employer on finding how far she had progressed.

In actual fact he didn't put in an appearance at all until late in the afternoon, just as she was tidying up before leaving to fetch Prue, and she waited patiently, and just a little defiantly, as he scanned the pages of typewritten information she had completed.

Finally he replaced the papers on her desk and raised his head. 'Is that *all* you've done?' he quizzed in a condescending tone.

It was just the type of comment Debra had been expecting and she slanted her chin distinctly higher, refusing to be forced on to the defensive. 'Yes! It's very complex work.'

'Excuses ... already?' His expression had a definite touch of sarcasm to it.

'No!' she denied fiercely, resentfully. 'There's nothing wrong with my typing speed, even if I do say so myself.' It was certain he never would! 'So I doubt if even my supposedly super-efficient predecessor could have done any more.'

'Not even if she only copied each reference sire's pedigree once, instead of every time?'

The implication might have been softly made, but its import rang inside Debra's head like a clanging bell of monstrous proportions, and her gaze started to waver doubtfully.

'You didn't say to do it only once,' she half accused, half protested. 'You merely said to copy out the relevant details of each animal's pedigree.'

'By which direction I assumed you would have the common sense to realise that I wouldn't be wanting a catalogue filled with repetitious information!' he gibed blisteringly. 'If you'd used your brain a little more that list could have been on its way to the printers this afternoon.'

'Then if it was so damned important that it leave today maybe you should have made your instructions a little more explicit!' she flashed, breathing hard, and stung by what she considered to be his unwarranted condemnation. If she had taken it upon herself to leave something out she was positive there would have been the devil to pay. 'Besides, surely one day isn't going to make that much difference. It will all be completed and checked by tomorrow.'

'Well, isn't that nice?' His sarcasm was almost tangible—that was, until it disappeared beneath an escalating anger. 'Especially since we only happen to get one mail a week in and out of Acacia Crossing!'

'How was I to know that?' Debra had no choice but to defend herself now. 'It might have helped if you'd told me.'

'I can't see how!' He picked up the papers from her desk and then dropped them again contemptuously. 'You obviously weren't capable of finishing it, anyway!'

'That's neither true nor fair!' she protested furiously. 'It would have been if you'd taken the trouble to explain it properly. Or don't you believe in accepting responsibility for *your* mistakes, Mr McAllister?'

Saxon's blue eyes glittered frostily at her attack. 'My only mistake, sweetheart, was in not overruling Eleanor's decision to hire you in the first place! That,' he flung a hand towards her painstaking efforts, 'isn't evidence of a mistake, but of ignorance. Your ignorance in not knowing the subject, of not being qualified to do the work, of not checking with last year's catalogue to see for yourself how much information was wanted!'

'I did try to find one!' she cried, her hands clenching at her sides, her nails digging painfully into her palms. 'But there weren't any in the filing cabinet or the cupboard.'

'So it didn't occur to you to try my desk!' he disparaged scornfully, wrenching open the bottom drawer and slapping a grey and orange booklet on to the inlaid leather centre. 'That would have been too much to expect, I suppose?'

Debra nodded, barely able to get her words past

the increasing lump of indignation in her throat. 'Under the circumstances, yes, it would!' she ground out tautly. 'If you'd happened to come in while I was searching your desk, I'm sure praising me for my initiative would have been the very last thought to enter your mind.'

'Oh? What then, in your opinion, would have been my reaction?'

'To accuse me of stealing or prying, most probably!'

'Two crimes totally unknown to you, of course!'

Oh, God, what was he accusing her of now? Sudden despair overwhelmed her like a smothering blanket, enveloping all her previously outraged emotions in a cocoon of helplessness and, needing desperately to escape, she turned blindly for the door.

'I—I'll be late for Prue,' she whispered shakily, and began half running towards the verandah on trembling legs.

Before she could push open the screen door a vice-like grip on her arm halted her headlong flight and she was spun around to stand with her back to the wall.

'You're not driving anywhere!' she was informed by a terse voice.

'Why, aren't I qualified enough to do that either?' Her head drooped forward listlessly.

'At the moment, too right you're not! You're more likely to run off the road and kill yourself.'

'And naturally you wouldn't want the ute damaged in such a fashion,' she gibed bitterly.

A rough hand ensnared her chin and jerked her face upwards. 'For a remark like that I could quite cheerfully dispose of you with my own two hands!' he rasped savagely. 'But, as beautiful a corpse as you'd make, I've no wish to have it on my conscience.'

'I didn't think you had one,' she attempted to laugh, only it broke in the middle.

'Then you would be wrong, wouldn't you?'

'Again?' she grimaced.

'Again,' he endorsed drily, his attractive mouth made even more appealing by its humorous upward curve.

Confused by her own emotional reaction to his smile, Debra centred her gaze on a less disturbing area—the darkly bronzed column of his throat. 'Prue will be wondering if I've forgotten her,' she murmured evasively.

'I doubt it, knowing my niece,' he contradicted wryly. 'She's more likely to be making the most of the extra time at her disposal.'

'Maybe,' she acceded weakly, pulling out of his grasp. His touch had been having a strangely hypnotic effect on her senses. 'But I'd still better be going.'

'Uh-uh!' Saxon shook his head emphatically. 'You can give it a miss for today. I'll send one of the men in for her.'

'But it is part of my job, and—and . . .'

'You don't intend to give me the opportunity of saying you're not capable in that regard as well?' he surmised ironically.

'Partly.' Her confession was selfconsciously made. 'But mainly because I had no intention of running off the road, anyway.'

'The conditions here not tough enough for that yet, hmm?'

The pupils of her violet eyes dilated nervously. Now what was he suggesting? That there was worse to come? Just the thought of it was enough to have her moving agitatedly from one foot to the other.

'Forget it!' he snapped suddenly, dragging a hand irritably around the back of his neck. 'And forget about driving in for Prue too. *I'll* see that she's collected.'

Without giving her an opportunity to reply—for the second time—Saxon pushed out through the screen door and strode down the steps from the verandah. Debra watched him leave with a soft lip caught indecisively between her teeth. Not only were her emotions completely jumbled now, but her thoughts were as well. His behaviour had been so totally out of character, and so unexpected, that she really hadn't a clue what to make of it!

CHAPTER FIVE

'YOU remember Anthea Devenish, don't you, Debra? You met at the Show in Brisbane.'

It was the day of the cricket match at Noonameena and the petite, brown-haired and hazel-eyed girl had begun making her way over to them immediately she saw the car pull up.

'Yes, of course,' Debra smiled politely in answer to Eleanor's query. And to the newcomer, 'It's nice to see you again.'

Which wasn't strictly true since she had found the other girl's attitude rather patronising the night they had been introduced, but, for the sake of propriety, she was willing to try and be friendly.

Evidently Anthea didn't feel under any such obligation, however, for the slight flickering of her lips could hardly have been called more than a perfunctory acknowledgment of the greeting and, with only a brief word for Eleanor and a condescending pat on the head for Prue, she made it all too plain just whose company she was seeking.

'Mac! I thought you were never going to arrive!' she exclaimed, a smile certainly to the fore now as she linked her arm proprietorially with his. 'Mummy and I only came home from the city yesterday and we brought my cousin Brendan with us. He's one of the Eldridges of Aurora Peak, you know. Do come and meet him.'

'Shortly, Anthea,' Saxon smiled back easily. 'I'll just take these things up to the homestead for Eleanor and then I'll be with you,' as he disengaged his arm from hers in order to open the luggage compartment of the car.

Debra moved forward, intending to help carry one of the hampers Sherry had carefully packed earlier that morning, but on reaching out to grip a handle found a male hand beating her to it.

'I'll take that for you,' Paul Bartlett offered cheerfully, his brown eyes telling her more adequately than words could have done that he was fully aware of the attractive picture she made in her close-fitting red slacks and white cotton top. 'We don't want to wear out your batting arm before the match even starts.'

'Thank you,' she smiled as they began heading for the house in a group, the men carrying the larger items and Prue commandeering the last small basket. 'But from that, do I assume that I'm on your team, after all?'

'No such luck, I'm afraid.' His response was accompanied by a wryly downcast expression. 'In the interests of fairness I really couldn't have put you down for any other side except Wyeera's. As it is, I've had to make up the number of females on your team with a couple of the girls from town.'

'Did you put Grandma's and my name down too?' chimed in Prue anxiously.

'I certainly did yours,' he grinned down at her, but to Eleanor's obvious relief went on to advise, 'although not your grandma's. I thought she would prefer to just watch.'

'Heavens, yes, and especially in this heat,' Eleanor added her own earnest thoughts on the matter. 'It's going to be a long hot day by the feel of it.'

Six heads nodded almost in unison in acknowledgment of that forecast, and then Anthea was calling coyly across from Saxon's other side, 'And whose team am I on . . . Mac's?'

Paul's mouth pulled in imperceptibly at the corners. 'Would I dare put you on any other?'

'I should hope not,' she retorted gaily, but with just the smallest hint of a bite to her voice. 'Otherwise I might refuse to play altogether!'

Everyone smiled politely at what Debra presumed was Anthea's attempted joke—even though she wouldn't have put it past the other girl to carry out her threat if Paul's answer hadn't been to her liking —and then, while the men took the hampers through to the kitchen, Eleanor began introducing Debra to those people who were making the most of their opportunity to relax in the cool comfort of the glassed-in verandah before the day's events got under way.

Not only were there families there from the surrounding district, as well as most of the population of Acacia Crossing, but some had travelled several hundred miles to participate in what had become an annual event, and there was an air of lightheartedness and festivity about the proceedings which struck an extremely responsive chord deep within Debra's system.

Perhaps because so many of them lived in such isolation and had to depend on their neighbours in times of need, they seemed like one enormous family when they came together on such occasions. A family wherein each member knew the abilities, and short-comings, of the others, but accepted them tolerantly because, in order to survive in such an unpredictable and often hostile environment, there was no other way.

It took Paul quite some time to marshall the various teams in the paddock beyond the homestead gardens where two strips had been slashed and mown to provide the necessary wickets—the rest of the grass left ankle-high because no one deliberately destroyed more feed than they had to when it might be vital to stock in the long summer months ahead. When Saxon won the toss and decided on his team being one of those to bat first, Debra retired to the house to help set up the tables and chairs which would be necessary for lunch beneath the shady cover provided by jacaranda, bauhinia, and pepper trees.

Nevertheless, it seemed hardly any time at all before one of the score-keepers was calling, 'Debra, you're on next!' and she found herself walking out across the sun-scorched paddock again to the accompaniment of calls from her fellow team members for good luck. Something, she wryly considered she would need a considerable amount of, since her partner at the other end was none other than her boss. If anything was going to make her nervous and destroy her concentration, he would!

Not that he would purposely make things difficult for her out there in front of everyone—that wasn't his way—but during the last week she had sensed that his attitude towards her had altered in some inexplicable and undefined manner. He still found fault with most of what she did, of course, but somehow his resentment of her presence wasn't quite so noticeable any more, with the result that her own guard had relaxed with each day that passed.

And it was the lessening of those defences which was causing most of her trouble now! Instead of being able to channel all her emotions into feelings of dislike and defiance, she was discovering them to be openly responding to a virile magnetism which both dismayed and annoyed her. Dismayed, because he was coming to occupy far too large a proportion of her thoughts, and annoyed, because even if she had been searching for a beau ideal—which she certainly wasn't!—then Saxon McAllister with his so vastly different background and upbringing would be the last person she'd choose to become infatuated with.

Determinedly, she made ready to receive her first ball and, as if venting her displeasure with herself on the red missile as it bounced towards her, she swung at it forcefully, if not stylishly, and cracked it straight over the heads of the inner fieldsmen. For a moment hardly anyone moved as surprise registered on all their faces, including Debra's, to see the ball bumping across the outfield with a lone figure in furious pursuit. Then a jubilant cheer rang out from those clustered at the rails and, recovering her senses, she began racing for the wicket at the other end of the pitch.

'You keep that up and we'll have them beaten in no time,' Saxon advised hastily as they passed each other the first time.

'I think it was a fluke!' she half laughed, half panted, when they crossed again.

'Well, whatever it was, try and repeat it ... often!'
he urged with a laugh on their third run.

Fortunately, at least for Debra, the ball had been
returned to the bowler by then, precluding their
need to run again, and she wiped the back of her
hand over her now perspiration-bedewed forehead
as she waited while Saxon faced the next ball.

After that their scores mounted steadily until, with
one last powerful sweep, Saxon reached the limit of
his allowed runs and had to retire. One of Wyeera's
stockmen quickly took his place, but after managing
to block a couple of balls he swung wildly at the following one and sent it straight into the hands of a
waiting fieldsman with nothing added to their total.
The next person to share the wicket with her was
Anthea.

Dainty, elegantly outfitted Anthea, who ambled
out to her place as if no one had anything better to
do than to wait on her convenience, and then made
such a performance about finding just the right spot
to stand that someone on the sidelines was impelled
to threaten in an exasperated voice, 'Get on with it,
or we'll start deducting points for holding up the
game!'

Anthea glared in the general direction of the homestead, brushed her hair back from her face with a
beautifully manicured hand, and finally took her
stance. But as it happened, Debra found her a harder
partner to play with than Saxon had been. Even if
he had nearly run her off her feet, at least she knew
when he called for her to run it was safe to do so.
With Anthea exactly the opposite was the case, and
after being dismissed for the first time because the

other girl started moving and then changed her mind and went back, leaving Debra to be stumped, she treated all her future calls with extreme caution—and some suspicion—when, after she had nearly done the same thing a second time, Anthea purred, 'I'm so sorry. I should hate to be the one to ruin your chance of a high score.'

I'm sure you would! grimaced Debra wryly to herself, but although she tried desperately hard to avoid it, the very next time she herself called for Anthea to run the other girl absolutely refused to move at all, and before Debra could return to her own end the ball had reached her wicket first.

'Oh, dear!' Anthea managed to look suitably remorseful. 'I suppose I should have run, but really ...' she fanned a delicate hand in front of her face, 'I don't think I could have made it. I'm just too out of breath.'

'That's all right,' Debra shrugged off the facetious-sounding apology evenly. It was only a game, after all, even though Anthea didn't look over-extended in the slightest. 'These things happen.'

'I'm just not much of a cricketer, I'm afraid.'

Debra merely smiled, perfunctorily, but didn't comment as she started back across the open paddock where she met Neale Stafford—Saxon's stud manager—as he came to take her place.

'Bad luck,' he commiserated, accepting the bat from her. 'We all thought you were going to make the limit.'

'The fates decreed otherwise,' she laughed over her shoulder as she kept walking.

Prue was the first to greet her and guided her to

where the others were sitting and talking beneath the trees. 'Gee, you were good,' she sighed with touching admiration. 'You got twenty-five runs.'

'Did I?' Debra smiled in surprise. She had lost count after the first few. 'That just goes to show what nice easy bowling can do to improve your game, doesn't it?'

'Saxon didn't seem to think so.'

'Oh? What makes you say that?'

'Because I heard him telling Grandma that he wished he had another six like you in the team.'

Debra's eyebrows flew upwards. That didn't sound like the Saxon she knew! She was more than half expecting to be thoroughly roasted for having allowed herself to be run out so easily. Twice!

'He was probably only joking,' she suggested lightly, then turned to acknowledge with a smile Pat Beasley's approving, 'That was a real good effort, lass!' as he sat waiting his turn for one of the other teams.

'An extremely good effort,' affirmed Eleanor sincerely as Debra literally sank down on an empty seat beside her. 'Would you like a drink, dear?'

'Yes, please!' she breathed fervently, her head nodding, her eyes closed. 'I think I could drink a bucket dry right at the moment.'

The older woman leant over to catch at her arm anxiously. 'I do hope it wasn't too much for you. I noticed you weren't wearing a hat.'

About to deny there was anything amiss—except that she was boiling hot and her throat bone-dry—Debra wasn't given an opportunity to do so, because immediately on perceiving his stepmother's worried gesture Saxon had broken off his conversation with a couple some short distance away and returned to Eleanor's side to question frowningly, 'What's wrong?'

On hearing his voice Debra promptly pushed herself upright, her eyes flashing open. 'Nothing's *wrong*,' she protested drily. 'I'm just thirsty, that's all.'

'Mmm, it was rather warm out there, wasn't it?' he agreed with such a slow smile that she had to close her eyes again in order to counteract the effect it was having on her. 'What would you like to drink?'

She shook her head absently. 'I don't really care, as long as it's cold and there's plenty of it.'

'I'll get you something,' offered Prue quickly, helpfully. 'I know where they are.'

'Thank you,' Debra smiled at her appreciatively. 'That's very kind of you, Prue.'

In her absence, and while Eleanor was distracted by a passing friend, Saxon perched his lithe length on the table beside Debra, his brilliant blue eyes never wavering from her heart-shaped face.

'You played very well,' he commended softly.

Horribly selfconscious all of a sudden, she shrugged deprecatorily. 'Not well enough to stop myself being stupidly run out.'

'I rather thought that wasn't altogether your fault.'

'No?' She stared at him, amazed. Surely he wasn't making excuses on *her* account! 'Well, I suppose we all get our signals crossed at some time or another.'

'So that's what happened.' He seemed to accept her explanation readily enough. 'Weren't you calling clearly enough?'

'Apparently not.' She took the line of least resistance. There was nothing to be gained in trying to convince him his lady friend wasn't of a particularly sporting disposition.

'I got you a jug of lemon with lots of ice in it!' Prue suddenly burst back on to the scene, a glass carafe in one hand and a tumbler in the other.

'Thank you, that looks delicious,' Debra smiled as she accepted the glass the child had filled for her and drank from it slowly, savouring every last refreshing drop. 'Aren't you having any?'

'No, I'm not thirsty,' Prue shook her head swiftly. Then, as her wandering gaze roved over the crowd, 'Oh, there's Jenny. I've been looking for her all morning,' and she was off in another direction before anyone had a chance to speak.

'From the way she fits in here it's obvious she's no stranger to Wyeera, or Acacia Crossing,' Debra commented thoughtfully as she watched the small figure disappear from sight.

'No, her parents often go away on these trips. This is the second time this year she's stayed with us,' Saxon revealed tolerantly.

'You don't mind?' as her eyes flicked up to his the light shone across them, turning them to a soft shade of lilac. 'I mean, it makes a lot of extra work for you, or one of your staff, to keep taking her to and from school each day.'

'Finding it a nuisance already, are you?'

A gibing harshness seemed to have settled about him which hadn't been there a moment before and she blinked in surprise. 'No, of course not!' she defended herself quickly, and vexed that he should have chosen to put such an interpretation on her remark. 'I rather enjoy my trips into town, as a matter of fact. It's just that I thought it would be less bother if she was enrolled for the School of the Air.'

One eyebrow quirked sardonically. 'Less bother for whom?'

He was being deliberately perverse, and she didn't know why! 'Well, for Prue, for a start,' she put forward tartly. 'Those journeys must be very tiring for her.'

'Out here there's younger children who have to make longer ones ... every day of the year.'

Debra clamped down on her rising temper only with difficulty. 'Maybe!' she retorted stormily. 'But I happened to have been talking about Prue. It must be hard for her to adapt to all those hours travelling whenever she comes here.'

'It's far less of a change than if she had to keep switching from a normal classroom situation to one of correspondence lessons coupled with the School of the Air at home,' he countered satirically. 'And *we* considered it was more important for the manner of her lessons to remain unchanged, rather than worry about the inconvenience it might cause one of our staff in driving her to school.'

The former point Debra was prepared to concede— now that he had finally made his way round to explaining it—but during the course of the conversation he appeared to have neatly turned her innocent enquiry into an attack on her personal willingness, and she sighed disconsolately. Obviously his attitude towards her hadn't so much changed over the last few days as it had been lying dormant!

'Oh, dear, have I missed anything?' Eleanor now turned to fix them with a querying gaze as her friend moved on. 'You are all right, Debra? The heat wasn't too much for you?'

'No, I'm fine, thank you, Eleanor,' she reassured the concerned woman quietly, although her accompanying smile wasn't quite as bright as it could have been. And hurriedly, in an effort to divert their attention elsewhere, 'Oh, look, I think Anthea's on her way back. I expect she'll be wanting something to drink as well.'

So she did, and while Saxon was away procuring a glass for her, the diminutive brunette arranged herself comfortably on a chair on Eleanor's other side.

'I really don't know why I let myself be talked into playing each year,' she immediately started to complain in long-suffering tones. 'It's not even as if I like the game.'

Debra suspected her employer provided the major incentive for the other girl's participation, but of course could hardly say so, and she left it to Eleanor to make a suitably appropriate comment. Which she did with considerable fervour.

'But it is for charity, Anthea,' she was reminded unequivocally. 'Those fees which everyone pays so they can play, and the sale of drinks and food provided by the Ladies' Auxiliary all goes for a very good cause. We raise a considerable amount of money throughout the year from days like this, and it also provides entertainment and an opportunity for everyone to gather socially, don't forget.'

Anthea didn't look as if she cared about meeting everyone socially. 'Oh, I suppose so,' she submitted less than enthusiastically, then altered her demeanour entirely when Saxon returned with another glass, which he filled and handed to her.

'Thank you so much,' she smiled up at him with such blatant eagerness that Debra had to turn away. 'Come and sit next to me so we can talk,' patting the seat beside her. 'We've hardly had a chance to say anything, except for that short time when you met Brendan. That's better,' she approved archly once he had complied with her request. 'Now, tell me how our team's going. Are we likely to win?'

For someone who only moments ago had been declaring how she disliked the game the change was quite startling, and Debra couldn't help her lips from curving wryly. Anthea was so obvious it was unbelievable! Or perhaps she just didn't care if all and sundry knew what her intentions were as long as she attained her goal. It was an obscurely dampening thought and one Debra didn't care to contemplate further, so it was with some relief, as well as genuine pleasure, that she noticed Paul and Neale Stafford walking towards them, together with Paul's sister Jeanne, who she had learnt that morning was Neale's fiancée.

'Have you all bitten the dust too?' she smiled as soon as they had pulled up chairs and seated themselves.

'Well, Neale and Paul didn't, they both scored the limit,' Jeanne relayed with a grin. 'But I'm afraid I rather let the side down somewhat.'

'Went for a duck, she did! No score at all,' Paul reproved with mock disgust.

'Mmm, I was so busy sneaking glances to see how

Neale was faring in the other game that I missed the ball completely, and before I knew it my middle stump had disappeared,' his sister explained impatiently.

'You're forgetting your first effort,' he prompted drily.

'Don't be nasty!' She wrinkled her nose at him goodnaturedly and confessed, 'I was partnering Dad at the time, and he'd just belted a beauty, so I immediately set off like a mad thing. The only trouble was,' she started to laugh, 'someone caught it, and by the time I realised what was happening, the ball had been returned and I was out as well.' Amid the ensuing laughter she turned to Debra. 'How many did you score?'

'Twenty-five, according to Prue.'

'It would probably have been more, except for me,' Anthea leant across to advise, sweetly apologetic. 'But I'm sorry to say I'm just not as fast and as athletic as Debra is. I'm more at home with golf, or one of those less vigorous sports. Although,' she was quick to add, 'I *do* admire those robust girls who can stand up to the rigours of men's games and play as their equals. It's just that I'm not one of them,' she smiled with feline satisfaction.

Having been made to feel like a cross between a greyhound and the Incredible Hulk, Debra looked down at her slim, one hundred and twenty pound, five foot six length, and shook her head wryly.

'I would hardly call it competing on equal terms with the men when they're bowling underarm,' she half laughed.

'No, of course it isn't!' Surprisingly, it was Eleanor

who broke into the conversation, her voice more vexed than Debra had ever heard it. 'It's utterly ridiculous to even suggest that might be the case, and I'm sure Debra would be the last person to want to compete under such conditions. I've never heard such nonsense in all my life!'

In the momentary silence which followed, Saxon's clear blue gaze locked with Debra's and she held his unfathomable glance with a slight defiance in her own. It wasn't her fault if his stepmother chose to champion his secretary instead of his lady friend!

Then he was turning to the older woman to drawl, 'Apart from the fact that I doubt very much if Anthea meant any harm by her remarks . . .'

Whereupon the red-faced girl at his side immediately confirmed, 'No! No, of course not!'

'I have the feeling that the chicken you're trying so hard to harbour beneath your wings, Eleanor, is more than capable of taking care of herself, should it be necessary,' he concluded with sardonic emphasis.

Although she looked considerably mollified, Eleanor apparently still wasn't altogether appeased, because she promptly sent him a frowning sideways glance and queried, 'Meaning?'

'Only that the next time *I* feel the sharp edge of her tongue won't be the first!' He subtly relieved the strained atmosphere by giving them something to laugh at. 'Believe me, if Debra considers you're out of line, she doesn't hesitate to let you know.'

'Good for you!' chuckled Jeanne delightedly, taking her cue from Saxon and keeping the talk flowing. 'We can't have these men believing they're infallible, can we?'

Debra smiled and agreed, but her eyes were wistful, and she only half heard Paul and Neale's bantering remonstrances. To defuse an awkward situation —for both his stepmother's and Anthea's sakes— Saxon had deliberately made it sound as if he was the one who came off worst in their encounters. Whereas, in actual truth, they both knew exactly the opposite was true. She had never managed to defeat him yet, and with a sinking feeling in the pit of her stomach, for the first time she really began to doubt if she ever could.

'Hey! Where have you drifted off to?'

Paul's laughing enquiry brought her back to the present sharply and had her shaking her head self-consciously on discovering herself to be the focal point for everyone's attention.

'Nowhere in particular,' she parried protectively, and urged a light smile to her lips. 'I was just day-dreaming, I guess. I'm sorry.'

'You're excused,' he pardoned her with a reciprocating grin. 'But Eleanor was just saying it's time to head for the house and help bring out the lunches. She thought you might like to go with her.'

'Oh, yes, of course. I said I would.'

'You don't have to, if you would rather sit here for a while longer,' Eleanor assured her kindly.

'No, really, I'd like to help.' Debra was on her feet before another suggestion to the contrary could be made. At least while she was working she would be able to occupy her mind with thoughts of other things besides her employer. 'Have they nearly finished?' nodding towards the players still out in the paddock.

'They probably will have by the time we've had our lunch.' It was Neale who answered her question. 'Then they'll have theirs while we're out in the field. We don't all stop to eat at the same time because we find it takes too long.'

Which, naturally enough, made lunch an extremely casual affair, with people coming and going as they pleased, stopping for something to eat and a talk, and then either going out to the paddock again or waiting, relaxed, for their turn with the bat.

It also made the meal stretch over a couple of hours or more, so that by the time all the ladies present had finished clearing the tables, the next innings was well on its way to being completed.

'By the way,' Jeanne said to Debra as they, together with Eleanor, resumed their seats beneath the trees, armed with some glasses and a jug of fresh orange juice this time. No one had protested when Anthea wandered off to join some other friends now that the object of her attention was fielding. 'Our monthly supper-dance is on in town next Saturday, in case you didn't know. Neale, Paul and I usually attend and I wondered if you'd like to come too.'

'Yes, I would like to,' Debra began, and then chewed at her lip doubtfully. 'Although I—I think I'd better check with Saxon first to see if it's okay with him.'

Jeanne's blue eyes widened in astonishment. 'Whatever for?'

'Well, I—we might be too busy for me to get away, what with the sale coming up, and all.' It didn't sound a particularly feasible reason, even to Debra, but without revealing the true state which existed between Saxon and herself there wasn't much else she could say.

'But surely not on a Saturday?'

'No, I shouldn't think so,' Eleanor added her weight to the discussion with a slight frown. 'Besides, hasn't Saxon been asked to judge the Brahman section at the Stratheden Show next Friday and Saturday?' Her eyes sought Debra's for confirmation.

'I—er—don't know. He hasn't mentioned anything about it to me.' When did he ever deign to tell her anything but the barest essentials? And then usually only at the very last minute.

'Well, I'm sure it will be all right, anyway,' Eleanor smiled encouragingly. 'You go ahead and make your arrangements and I'll explain to Saxon. It's good for you to get away from the property every so often.'

'But I do that twice each school day,' Debra laughed. 'And I accompanied you to your Ladies' Auxiliary and Garden Club meetings last week.'

'So you did.' Eleanor patted her arm softly, gratefully. 'I don't know what I would have done without those notes you made for me. I'm afraid I forget so many things these days unless I write them down immediately.'

'Oops, there goes another of your opposition, Debra,' interposed Jeanne with a chuckle, seeing another batsman head back towards the homestead. 'It shouldn't be long now till we find out who's going to be in the play-off.'

'Have you any ideas which teams they're likely to be?'

The other girl shrugged and grinned. 'Your guess

is as good as mine, although Wyeera were scoring pretty well early in their innings.'

'But not Noonameena?'

'Not while I was around, that's for sure!' came the laughing response. 'I was talking to Mike Allworth—you know, from Simmonds' Primary?—while we were clearing up, though, and he reckoned Acacia Crossing had also begun strongly this year, so it might be the two of you in the final. It doesn't look as if Town and Country are posing much problem for your bowlers at the moment.' She paused and held up an arresting hand. 'But back to Saturday. How about you drive over here with Neale, have dinner with us, and then we can all go in together? That's what we usually do.'

'It sounds fine to me—and thank you,' Debra smiled her gratitude. 'I might enjoy the drive to town during the day, but I'm not so sure I'd like it on my own at night.'

'Oh, there's no need to worry. Even if you did get stranded someone would come to look for you if you hadn't arrived at your destination within a reasonable time,' Jeanne imparted her information with a nonchalance born of familiarity. 'And we don't have any Min Min lights round here to make your nervous. They're further north.'

'Min Min lights?' Debra repeated dubiously.

'Mmm, haven't you heard of them?' Jeanne warmed to her subject with a gleeful impishness. 'They're very bright lights which suddenly appear out of nowhere at night, but no one knows for certain just what they are, or what causes them, because they only come *so* close and then—poof!' she snapped her fingers quickly, 'they go out ... and re-appear behind you!'

'You're having me on!'

'No, honestly, that's what they've been known to do,' she vowed seriously. 'People who have been stopped on the road at night say they've thought they were the headlights of another car coming towards them, only they never quite make it right to you, but go out and then reappear somewhere else. Often behind you. Apparently the Aboriginals have know about them for generations,' she went on informatively, 'but the first white person to see one—so the story goes—was a stockman coming home one night when suddenly this bright light reared up from behind a tombstone in the local cemetery—sending his horse berserk—and scaring the living daylights out of him. He promptly galloped hell for leather to the Min Min hotel, hence the name, and the damned light chased him the whole way there.'

'And no one knows what they are?' sceptically.

'There's been lots of suggestions,' Jeanne shrugged insouciantly. 'Spontaneous combustion of gases from bore-heads, natural phenomena brought about by atmospheric variations, birds with a phosphorescent substance on their wings ... oh, all sorts of weird and wonderful ideas, but no one has yet been able to say definitely what it is because no one's been able to get close enough to find out. Some people have even tried chasing *them*, but as fast as you go forwards, they keep moving away. Then, as I said, they disappear and come to life again somewhere else.'

Still not knowing quite whether to believe her or not, Debra looked to Eleanor for corroboration.

'Yes, it's quite true,' she nodded, and smiled. 'They call the area where they occur the Boulia Triangle.'

'As long as it's not the Acacia Crossing Triangle,' Debra laughed. 'I imagine it could be quite eerie to come across something like that on a lonely road in the middle of the night.'

Subsequently, their talk turned to less puzzling subjects, although with the number of people stopping to pass the time of day and renew acquaintanceships it wasn't surprising that their conversations were inclined to be disjointed.

'Now, where was I?' questioned Jeanne humorously following one such interruption, then she pulled a wry face. 'Never mind, I don't think I'll even try to remember. It looks as if your opponents have been accounted for at last, Debra. Here comes Saxon and Neale. How did it go?' she asked of the two men as they joined them.

'Pretty good,' Neale grinned, rumpling her hair fondly as he took the seat next to her. 'We beat them by more than fifty runs.'

All too conscious of Saxon's powerful frame occupying the chair beside herself, Debra determinedly kept her face half turned in Neale's direction. 'You've made the final, then?' she asked interestedly.

'*We*'ve made the final,' Saxon's deeply modulated voice contradicted lazily. 'Or aren't you a part of this team any more?'

'Yes, of course I am!' Debra automatically swung round before she realised what she was doing, and her eyes flashed with sudden understanding as soon as they connected with the taunting look in his. He had said that for the sole purpose of making her face him! With a deep steadying breath she eyed him challengingly from beneath ebony lashes. She hadn't given up the battle yet! 'Unless you would rather replace me with someone else, that is,' she breathed eloquently, knowing full well he would be aware she wasn't only referring to the cricket.

'Not likely!' hooted Neale in the background. 'Right at this moment Mac wouldn't trade you for the world.'

There was no need for words. Debra just allowed the barest arching of her brows to do her questioning for her, and was rewarded by a slow, wryly curving smile which flipped her heart over with a perturbing ease.

'As the man says ... what would we do without you?' he drawled.

It was a minor victory only; Debra had no illusions about that. But coming as it did after such a surplus of defeats she was more than satisfied. In public, at least, it seemed not all the advantages were his, and from now on, she decided, if it was at all possible she would be using that knowledge in order to bring a little more balance into what had been, until now, a very one-sided situation.

Presently Paul rejoined them as well, his face a study of rueful regret as he advised, 'That's the finish of us for today, I'm sorry to say.'

'We lost?' his sister quizzed.

'We were thrashed,' he amended drily, bringing smiles to the faces of his listeners. 'As unbelievable as it may seem, our bowling was even worse than our batting. They didn't even need their full innings to put us out of the game.'

'Oh, well, at least my loyalties won't be divided now. I can cheer for Neale with a clear conscience,' Jeanne advised happily. 'Besides which, I can't honestly say I'm sorry I don't have to go out there again in this heat. It is unseasonably hot today, isn't it?'

Her encompassing glance brought forth agreement, and then Saxon was rising to his feet. 'In the meantime, I guess I'd better start rounding up our people again.' His eyes were already roaming over the various groups and concentrations. 'It sounds as if it might be a long play-off.'

Which was exactly what it turned out to be, with each run being fiercely contested and, as a result, the scores being kept to a minimum. When their innings was finally completed—and having achieved a total which, although it caused no great despair among their ranks, certainly didn't give anyone reason to cheer either—Wyeera set about fielding in determined fashion. However, when Acacia Crossing's score began to inexorably close the gap, Saxon and one of the other team members returned for reinforcements, and as one headed for a particular section of the crowd, the other made for those beneath the trees.

'Come on, we need all the help we can get,' Saxon owned with a laugh as he caught hold of Debra's wrist and tugged her out of her chair. 'They're getting too close for comfort.'

Accepting his action in good part, a sweep of her hand included Eleanor and Jeanne. 'Mmm, we were only saying a while ago that we wouldn't be surprised to hear a call go out for all hands to the wheel.'

'She's being too polite,' gurgled Jeanne irrepressibly beside them. 'What we really said, was ... that it looked as if the men had got themselves into a difficult position and would need the help of the fairer sex to pull them out of it ... as usual.'

'Is that so?' His eyes narrowed mock-threateningly. 'Well, I'll leave Neale to take you to task for that impertinence, young lady,' he promised her tauntingly. 'But as for this one,' his attention turned to Debra and a muscular arm across her shoulders imprisoned her against his side, 'I'm sure I'll be able to devise some fitting punishment myself.'

'Such as?' she dared to ask as they left the others behind.

Saxon lowered his head confidingly, disturbingly close. 'Now that, as they say, would be telling,' he mocked. 'Suffice for you to know that ...'

'What about me?'

The somewhat peevish-sounding interruption had him swinging around to face its originator with Debra still firmly pinned to his side.

'Don't you want my help too?' Anthea now enquired sharply, her expression hostile as it raked over the slim figure pressed against him.

'I wouldn't dream of asking you, Anthea,' he returned easily, pacifyingly. 'Those manicured hands of yours aren't meant for fielding a cricket ball.'

While the other girl simpered appropriate words and basked in the warmth of his obvious concern, Debra looked down at her own slender fingers and grimaced dourly. Hers weren't exactly a calloused bunch of fives either, but presumably that didn't matter!

Her gesture evidently hadn't gone unnoticed, however, for as they resumed walking Saxon smiled and disclosed wryly, 'I wanted someone I could rely on and who would at least make an attempt to stop the ball.'

'Ah, yes, my robust constitution again,' she quipped sardonically.

'Don't be such a damned fool! I didn't mean it that way, and you know it,' he retorted roughly, and abruptly spinning her loose. 'There's a lot of words I could use to describe you, sweetheart, as you should be aware by now, but ...' pausing, his vivid blue eyes slid appraisingly over every shapely contour, 'I can assure you, robust certainly isn't the one which springs to mind.'

Two bright stains of colour flared into her smooth cheeks and she dropped her gaze in embarrassment. 'I wasn't fishing for compliments,' she disclaimed selfconsciously.

'Did I say you were?'

'N-no, but ...'

'Then let's forget about Anthea's unthinking comments, hmm?' A hand beneath her chin ensured she couldn't avoid looking at him for any longer. 'We have a cricket match to win, Miss Armitage, and, you being my secretary, I'm expecting a hundred per cent effort from you,' he teased lightly.

'Yes, sir,' she nodded, swallowing convulsively. That fascinating smile of his could hold her spellbound so effortlessly it wasn't funny!

In the paddock Debra took her place, along with

another couple of the female members of the team who had volunteered to field, and concentrated on the game. From a spectator's point of view the finish, as it crept relentlessly closer, couldn't have been more exciting. But for the players, on both teams, it was fraught with tension. Acacia Crossing were down to their last batsmen—one more out and Wyeera would win—but they were also only three runs behind, and if they succeeded in making those runs the decision would be reversed.

There wasn't one pair of eyes on Noonameena that afternoon that wasn't watching—even the children had stopped their play in order to line the fence— as one of Saxon's young stud grooms came up to bowl what everyone knew would be the last balls of the match. Debra looped her hair back behind her ears to make certain her vision wasn't impaired at an inopportune moment and waited tensely as the ball left the bowler's hand and flew towards the stocky batsman awaiting its delivery. When he merely blocked it a concerted sigh of relief went up from the fielders, and then they each went through their preparatory routines again.

The next time the bat connected with the ball with such a resounding crack that everyone immediately knew that this could be their last chance.

'For God's sake, *someone* catch it!' yelled a voice from near the wicket, and suddenly, out of a clear blue sky, Debra saw it zooming straight towards her.

With a choked gasp she instinctively put out her hands—it was either that, or collect it right in the midriff—and felt it slam into them with a force that sent her staggering two steps backward. Not until the cheers of jubilation started to ring out and the first of her team-mates raced over to congratulate her did she realise she was still holding the ball, and it was with a somewhat taut expression that she accepted their elated words of praise.

Saxon was the one who eventually drew her away from them, a knowing look on his face as he quizzed, 'How are the hands?'

Her reply was quite explicit, and not altogether facetiously uttered. 'Am I allowed to scream now, or do I have to wait until after we leave?'

'That bad?'

'I don't think they've got an unbroken bone between them,' she half laughed flippantly.

'Then perhaps you'd better let me have a look,' he suggested with a frown. 'It's quite possible you could have broken or dislocated a bone somewhere.'

She shook her head quickly, dismissively. 'No, really, I'm exaggerating, they're okay. My fingers *can* all still move.' She gave a wry grimace and owned, 'It's just that I prefer them not to right at the moment.'

'All right, we'll leave it for now,' he smiled wryly in understanding. 'But they'd better have improved by the time we go, or it will be a different story.'

'They will.' Her prediction was confident. 'In fact, they have already. See?' As she raised one slightly cupped member and viewed it with a dispassionate grin. 'It's only bright pink now instead of vermilion.'

A short laugh and Saxon was eyeing her consideringly, his head angled slightly to one side. 'You're a complex little character, aren't you, sweetheart?' he mused.

Taken completely unawares by the sudden switch in the conversation, Debra immediately became defensive and shrugged. 'I don't know what you mean.'

'No?' The peak of his brows became more noticeable. 'Well, maybe you don't at that,' he acceded ruefully before reverting to their original topic by observing, 'It looks as if there's quite a reception committee waiting for you,' seeing Eleanor and Jeanne, together with Prue—and Anthea—waiting beside the fence.

'For *us*, you mean,' she corrected drily. She knew who Anthea was waiting for, and it certainly wasn't herself!

Whether he caught her meaning and replied, Debra didn't hear, because as soon as they had passed through the gateway Prue was excitedly catching at her arm, her exclamation of admiration soon becoming submerged beneath less vociferous, but just as sincere, congratulations from the rest of Wyeera's supporters, all of which she accepted self-consciously.

'It was only one catch, after all,' she remarked wryly to Jeanne a short while later as they all began heading for the homestead verandah and the presentations. 'And an accidental one, to boot. I put up my hands to protect myself ... catching the ball was the last thing I had in mind.'

'Oh, dear, what a thoroughly disappointing discovery, when here we all were thinking how utterly brave and sporting you'd been,' cooed Anthea from

where she was walking a few paces behind them—
with Saxon—and obviously referring to what she had
overheard. 'It seems you've been accepting our congratulations and admiration under false pretences,
Debra.' Her laugh tinkled maliciously.

Not yours, at any rate, since you haven't yet offered
any, grimaced Debra to herself. By way of a reply,
however, she simply hunched one shoulder in an unconcerned gesture and endorsed laconically, 'My
sentiments entirely.'

'Well, I still think it was a damned good effort, no
matter what the reason,' Jeanne turned back to an-
nounce loyally.

'But of course it was,' Anthea agreed in syrupy
tones. 'In fact, I very much doubt if there's another
woman here who could have done it at all, let alone
with such—er—flair.' That laugh trilled forth once
more. 'I mean to say, it's just as well not everyone
prefers to remain cool and relaxed on the sidelines
like languid little me, isn't it?'

Meaning that I look hot and bothered, supposed
Debra sardonically, and felt like reminding the girl
behind her that, originally, she hadn't been languid
at all—but *piqued*—when she'd thought she was being left out of the game. But she didn't, she just sighed
and kept walking. Nothing Anthea said could possibly drop her stock any lower than it already was
with Saxon, so she had absolutely nothing to gain by
becoming involved in any of Anthea's venomous
little word-plays.

There was no formality about the presentations
whatsoever once they got under way. They were
strictly for enjoyment, and the winners' dozen bottles

of champagne were very quickly disposed of, and not only by the team members, as were the cartons of canned beer awarded to the runners-up. All in all, it was a very pleasant, easy-going finish to what had been an extremely agreeable day for the most part, although Debra did experience one uncomfortable moment when Saxon was accepting the small cup which accompanied the win.

'You'd better marry that young secretary of yours, Mac, to ensure she's on your team for a long time to come. You would've been lost without her today!' shouted someone humorously from among the crowd.

Debra promptly flushed scarlet and bit at her lip as the ensuing laughter flowed round her. Her eyes, wide and almost purple in colour, flew unerringly to a suntanned face and hovered there apprehensively. How humiliating it would be if, in an effort to make certain no one else was tempted to make comments of a like nature, Saxon told them exactly how he did feel about her presence on Wyeera!

In a brief second their glances crossed, returned, held, and she released a shuddering sigh of relief. There was a mocking light in those blue depths, but no rancour—as was proved when he faced the crowd again, an answering smile on his lips.

'You're certainly right on your second count, Alan,' he was prepared to concede drily. 'But as to your first ... well, give the girl credit for having more sense than to take on a corner country cattle-man. I doubt if she'd have me.'

A tactful reply and what could have been an embarrassing situation was passed over smoothly. But

as the laughing crowd began to disperse Debra turned
to Eleanor with a slight frown puckering her forehead.

'Corner country?' she sought elucidation.

'Mmm, that's right, Haddon Corner. You know,
where the States of Queensland and South Australia
meet.'

'Oh, yes, of course.' Her smile was rueful. 'I should
have realised. Perhaps while I'm out this way I
should make the effort and go and see it. Is there
anything much there?'

'Just a post,' supplied Eleanor so drily that they
both laughed.

Now that the presentations were concluded everyone began their preparations for leaving and on one
of his trips to and from the homestead, putting the
equipment away, Paul stopped beside Debra with
some folding chairs tucked beneath his arm.

'By the way, did Jeanne mention anything to you
about the dance in town on Saturday?' he asked.

She nodded. 'Yes, she did, as a matter of fact.'

'Would you like to come?'

'Very much,' she smiled up at him engagingly.
'I'm ...'.

'I hope that's not *next* Saturday you're talking
about, old son,' Saxon's deeply voiced insertion cut
her words short and had them both looking to where
he was fastening one of Eleanor's hampers for her.

'Why not?' Paul half frowned, half smiled.

'Because next Saturday Debra will be in Stratheden, with me.'

Considering that was the first time he had even
mentioned it to her, it was only natural that Debra

should look somewhat surprised, but then, as she covertly studied her employer's slightly mocking features, her eyes began to narrow in suspicion. Had he made that decision before, or *after*, Paul stopped to speak to her? She certainly wouldn't put it past him to be using it solely as a means of making her life less enjoyable.

It must have seemed strange to Paul too, because he promptly laughed and urged, 'Come off it, Mac! You don't need a secretary while you're away judging, and you've sure never taken one with you before.'

'Maybe not,' Saxon conceded, and without changing his expression in the slightest. 'But then they didn't need the experience. They were already conversant with the cattle business before coming to Wyeera.'

The corners of Paul's mouth turned down wryly. 'And just what experience can Debra get at Stratheden that she can't get here? Hell, you've got the biggest Brahman stud for miles around. What else does she need to know about?'

'With the sales coming up, a great many things, as you should know,' Saxon returned evenly, his composure unruffled. 'However, until now no one's had the time to teach her, so ...'

'You decided on the Show at Stratheden as being a good opportunity to fill her in on the details,' Paul concluded ruefully for himself.

'Sorry, feller, but business comes before pleasure,' with a sympathetic grin.

Paul expelled a heavy breath and swung back to Debra. 'It looks as if we'll have to take a raincheck on it, I'm afraid,' he smiled. 'How about next month instead?'

'I'll make sure I'm available.'

She wasn't quite sure just how she could guarantee that, but she was determined to have a damned good try! Saxon's answers might have sounded plausible to his friend, but she still wasn't entirely convinced. There was a background to the situation that Paul didn't know about, and the more she considered it the more sceptical she became.

She was still turning it over in her mind during their journey back to the property, or at least, she was, until the arrival of low black clouds on the horizon heralded the storm which everyone had been predicting would follow such an unseasonably hot day, and her thoughts flew off at a tangent—as they had so many times before on such occasions—to dwell on memories from long ago.

CHAPTER SIX

Awake, Debra had some chance of dispelling her distressing thoughts, but asleep, she had no such control, and the images she had tried so hard to forget flooded back with insidious persistence. It was the storm which had triggered their return, and although it hadn't brought much rain it had been noisy, was still noisy, and she tossed and turned feverishly at every jarring reverberation.

In her dreams she was back on that small boat again with her parents, watching as the sudden unexpected squall turned the blue skies to black and the glass-like sea into white-capped troughs. She could see again too the look of fear on her mother's face as that freak wave appeared out of nowhere to tower over them and she made a frantic grab for her only child. Then there was nothing—only a grey blank—until Debra had woken up in hospital, crying, and complaining her head hurt.

Perspiration soaked tendrils of hair clung to her temples and she moaned softly, trying to deny the onset of the scene she knew would follow as unchangingly as night follows day.

Initially, there was that terrifying shock to be experienced of being woken from a peaceful sleep by the chilling sound of screeching metal as the roof of their car buckled beneath the weight of the fallen telegraph pole, followed by Rose Armitage's broken scream. A scream Debra had echoed in blind panic when a flare of jagged lightning illuminated the devastated interior of the vehicle and she began struggling helplessly to claw her way out.

Then, as now, there had been a strong pair of hands to restrain her, but whereas the voice which accompanied them should have been warning, 'For God's sake, lie still, little one! We can't get you out at the moment, there's live wires everywhere!' it was commanding instead, 'For God's sake, Debra, wake up!'

Abruptly her eyes flew open and she lay there unmoving as her mind registered—with the aid of the light beaming into the room from the well lit hallway—Saxon's broad shape as he sat on the edge of the bed leaning over her, his shirt completely unbuttoned as if he had been in the act of undressing, or, after having removed it, had thrown it back on again in a hurry. For a time the only sound was that made by her harsh, ragged breathing, but then a sob of reaction escaped her and she pressed her face into the pillow in an attempt to supress the onslaught she feared might follow.

'I—I'm sorry if I disturbed y-you,' she apologised so huskily he had to bend his head even lower to hear. 'I'm all r-right now, th-thank you.'

'Are you?' His voice grated sharply in the strained silence, his hand no less rough when it forced her to face him again.

'Oh, please!' The entreaty was torn from her as she felt that suffocating lump rise into her throat again. 'Please! Can't you just leave me alone!' she cried, trying frantically to push herself upright and further away from him.

'No!' he lashed back at her furiously, his fingers digging punishingly into her arms as he dragged her to within inches of his rigidly held form. 'There's too much about you that needs explaining already. Now I want to know just what it is that has you breaking out in a cold sweat and screaming in absolute terror.'

'What's the point?' Her efforts to free herself drained the last reserves of her strength and her head drooped forward defeatedly as an uncontrollable attack of weeping overtook her. 'You wouldn't believe me, anyway. You never do!' she choked.

'Oh, hell!' Saxon slid his arms around her tightly, comfortingly, drawing her shaking figure closer to the muscular wall of his chest and cradling her head against his shoulder. 'I've been too successful in my intentions, haven't I, sweetheart?'

Debra didn't reply. Even if she had wanted to she wouldn't have been able to, for now that her tears had started they were impossible to stop. Sagging against him weakly, she could only wait for them to run their natural course, and let the hand which was stroking her hair so gently calm her troubled spirit as best it could.

'Now will you tell me what it was that frightened you so badly?' he asked softly when, after one last shivering sigh, she lay quietly against him.

She went to pull away and then changed her mind. It *was* comforting with him holding her as he was, and she liked the feel of his firm skin beneath her cheek, so why should she move?

'It was only a dream,' she murmured throatily.

'But a recurring one, hmm?'

Her long lashes flickered briefly against his shoulder. 'H-how did you know?'

'I guessed,' he disclosed deeply, his fingers massaging the nape of her neck now. 'When the storm arrived you became so edgy that I figured it must have had some special significance for you, and yet it just as obviously wasn't the storm itself. You showed no fear of that at all.' His hand continued to work its relaxing magic. 'So, when you screamed as you did in your sleep and I found you moving about so wildly, it immediately made me wonder if perhaps premonition hadn't been the underlying cause of your restlessness.' He paused and his brows drew together in a frown. 'Does this always happen when there's a storm?'

'No, not always,' she admitted with a poor attempt at a laugh. 'Mainly when there's a lot of lightning around.'

'But why?' He eased away from her in order to cup her face between his two hands. 'What happened that was so dreadful it scares you half to death when you dream about it?'

'Please don't ask me.' She stared at him miserably, begging him to understand. 'I've lived through it once tonight already, I don't want to do it again.'

The line of his jaw hardened fractionally. 'But you can't go through the rest of your life keeping something like this to yourself, and dreading every storm that might come along!'

'At least that's better than letting everyone know

what a jinx I am!' she blurted defensively, and then inhaled a dismayed breath on seeing his increased interest.

'A minx, yes, but surely not a jinx!' he teased lightly.

It gave Debra the excuse she needed to retreat and she took it swiftly. 'See, I said there was no point in telling you. I knew you wouldn't believe me!'

'Uh-uh,' he vetoed, his head moving slowly from side to side. 'You don't back out of it that easily, sweetheart. I just happen to believe we make our own luck, and spellbinding though you may be at times, I can't quite bring myself to picture you as an instrument of misfortune. However ...' he fixed her with a penetrating glance devoid of all humour, 'I do mean to discover *why* you choose to see yourself in such a role.'

She sighed dully. 'Because it's true, that's why. Because everyone I've ever cared about has—has ...'

'Died?'

Not even by pressing her eyelids tightly closed could she prevent the tears from squeezing underneath them. 'Been killed,' she corrected tremulously.

'How?' He drew her gently back to him again.

It was obvious he wasn't going to let the matter drop until he knew the whole story and so, with her forehead buried against his chest and her fingers clutching at his open shirt for support, she told him what she had never told anyone else before.

'There was a—a boy at the orphanage t-too,' she continued jerkily afterwards. 'He was only six, but we used to pretend we r-really were brother and sister, but even he—even he ...'

'Sssh!' Saxon soothed close beside her temple. 'You don't have to go on.'

'He ran out from behind the bus on his way home from school one day, right into the path of a passing car,' she concluded tonelessly.

Tipping her face up to his with a long forefinger, he laid a kiss at the corner of her trembling lips. 'You haven't exactly had a very happy life so far, have you, sweetheart?' he pondered soberly.

Debra's hands clenched harder on the material of his shirt. 'I w-wasn't asking for s-sympathy.'

'I know.' His lips found her tear-stained cheeks this time. 'But I didn't have to take it on myself to make it a damned sight more miserable for you, though, did I?' in tones of self-disgust.

'I wasn't asking for your pity either,' she denied huskily.

'I know that too,' he smiled ruefully. 'But I also know those accidents concerning your family were just that ... accidents! You're no evil spirit, sweetheart, believe me,' he tried to impress on her earnestly.

'I might just as well be, the result's the same,' she charged dejectedly. 'Even you said I was an undesirable.'

'But for quite another reason,' he promptly reminded her in wry accents. The tips of his fingers brushed lightly against the side of her neck as he began threading them through her hair, and his shapely mouth feathered across her softly parted lips. 'I also said you looked very *des*irable, if you recall.'

Already in a highly emotional state, her senses now began to reel beneath a force she had never before experienced and she trembled as she half swayed towards him, unknowingly provocative.

'And was that for quite another reason too?' she quizzed shakily.

'No, that was because I keep getting the urge to take you to bed with me,' Saxon only just found time to reveal before his mouth closed relentlessly over hers.

It wasn't the first time he had kissed her, of course. He had arbitrarily seen to that in Brisbane. But this time was nothing like the first and as her bloodstream turned to molten fire Debra didn't fight to be free, as she had before, but responded with a willingness which both bewildered and startled her. Relinquishing her grip on his shirt at last, she smoothed her fingers savouringly, sensuously, over the sinewed flesh of his chest and shoulders to twine them within the tousled hair at the back of his head, and making no protest when he lowered her to the pillow.

Briefly, his lips left hers to scorch a mesmerising path to the vulnerable hollow at the base of her throat, then returned to claim them again with a hungry possessiveness which sent waves of desire rolling over her and left her drowning within a sea of uncontrolled emotion.

A caressing hand explored the flaring curves of hip and waist, then travelled higher to close about a tautly rounded breast. At the unaccustomed touch Debra moved against him shakenly, ripples of tingling sensation racing along her nerves, and then suddenly she was free as Saxon pulled sharply away from her and rose swiftly to his feet, all in the one lithe action.

His breathing was heavy and uneven as he raked a hand savagely through his hair. 'I'm sorry. It wasn't my intention to take advantage of your already unguarded state,' he apologised in a rough, jarring voice, and turned for the door. 'I'll see you in the morning.'

'Saxon!' Still recovering from the rush of feeling which had enveloped her, Debra called after him plaintively as she started to her knees. 'Please don't leave. I—I'm scared of going back to sleep again in case my dream returns.'

He wheeled to face her furiously, an air of rigid self-discipline emanating from him, his face in darkness with his back to the doorway. 'So what are you suggesting? That I make love to you for the rest of the night in order to keep you awake?'

She bowed her head embarrassedly, but the remembered security his arms had afforded impelled her onwards. 'Couldn't you just ... hold me? Like you did before,' she whispered throatily.

'Are you being cute, or deliberately naïve?' His tone was mercilessly cutting.

'N-neither,' she faltered miserably. 'I just wanted ...'

'Well, I don't! And nor do I care for being propositioned, thanks ... no matter how ingenuously!' he stated with acid contempt, preparing to leave for the second time.

Propositioned! Twin flags of burning humiliation and anger vied for precedence in Debra's crimson cheeks and grabbing the only thing to hand, her pillow, she hurled it towards the closing door with all her might.

'*Get out*, you lowdown, despicable swine!' she yelled. Superfluously, since he had already departed. 'Just get out and leave me alone,' she continued in less forceful but decidely more tearful tones. And, throwing herself face down among the rumpled sheets began to cry helplessly, 'I hate you, hate you, hate you ...!'

Debra pushed her foot down harder on the accelerator and smiled as the powerful ute responded immediately. She had just dropped Prue off at school and she was in a hurry to get back to the property. There was a lot of work she had to finish before leaving for Stratheden with Saxon the next morning and she wanted to get started on it as soon as possible.

Thinking of her employer had her lips twisting into a wry grimace and she cast her mind back ruefully over the preceding three days. If anything, Saxon's attitude seemed to have hardened since that disastrous interlude in her bedroom. The man who had originally comforted her so considerately, totally unrecognisable in the cool sardonic person who had greeted her the following day.

Whether or not he had reverted to his customary gibing manner because of what he mistakingly believed to have been her uninvited advances, she dreaded to contemplate, but conversely, due to a surfeit of pride as well as a continuing sense of mortification over the whole affair, she point-blank refused to say anything which might refute the suggestion.

In the distance a red cloud of dust approached and she watched it idly. Road-trains weren't a novelty to her any more, but they fascinated her all the same, and when the huge trailers roared towards her in a storm of flying dust and scattered stones—the sound of the horn indicating the driver recognised the ute —she acknowledged the signal with a smile and a ready wave. Everyone who used the road knew everyone else's vehicles and even she could discern some of the more regular travellers now.

Suddenly, as the last of the trailers passed her, however, there came a report as if a gun had been fired nearby, making her jump involuntarily. Then, before her widening eyes, the windshield disintegrated into a jigsaw of frosted, shattered glass, and she knew that one of those stones had been bigger and had hit harder than the rest.

Instinctively, she went for the brake—what with the dust *and* the crazy paving glass it was impossible to see where she was going—but she must have been overly zealous in her application because the ute immediately began to slew sideways on the loose surface, and before she could attempt to correct the swing she could feel it sliding over the banked shoulder of the road at a precarious angle and careering out of control down to the water-table below, where it was brought up short with a jolting crash which promptly showered half of the fractured windshield down on top of her.

For a moment she sat there too stunned to move, just thankful to be still capable of breathing, and then as she released her safety belt and shakily inched her way out of the vehicle sent up a prayer of gratitude for the inventor of the safety process which allowed glass to fragment into small pieces devoid of sharp edges. She had a couple of nicks and scratches from it tumbling down on her, but nothing compared to what it could have been if those segments had been jagged.

After thoroughly surveying the damage she sighed despondently. Although the bull-bar at the front appeared to have protected the engine satisfactorily when they had collided with the tree which had curtailed their runaway progress, the rear of the ute was still unhealthily slanted towards the top of the slope, while one of the front tires had been ripped to shreds on a small but vicious-looking tree stump on the way down. And not only that, but somewhere along the way the tail-gate had burst open and all the groceries she had picked up in town for Sherry were now scattered indiscriminately over the embankment.

So now what did she do? The angle at which the ute was balanced precluded any effort on her part to move it either up, or down, the bank, and even if she had known how to—which she didn't—she couldn't have changed the tire for the same reason. All she could do, she finally decided, was to keep an ear pricked for anyone coming along the road in order to flag them down for help, and in the meantime to recover Sherry's groceries as best she could and tidy up the mess the glass had made in the cabin.

Stopping only occasionally for a mouthful of water from the canvas bag attached to the front of the vehicle, Debra toiled on amid the uncanny silence and beneath an increasingly hot sun. Not even the tree provided any protection, for the shade was being thrown away from where she was working, and it wasn't long before trickles of perspiration began plastering her shirt to the middle of her back. A couple of times she had stopped to listen, thinking she might have heard a car approaching, but each time she guessed they must have been figments of her imagination brought on by the solitude and she had returned to what she was doing while wondering if anyone beside herself and the road-train intended using the highway that day.

It was going on for lunchtime before she could distinguish the definite rumbling of wheels in the distance heading towards town, and she scrambled up the slope with a light of relieved anticipation shining in her eyes, only to find she had a surprisingly long wait for the vehicle to come into view. Sound travelled much further than she realised in that quiet stillness.

As soon as her eyes focused upon it, though, some of her anticipation was replaced with another feeling entirely. Unless she was very much mistaken that was Wyeera's Range-Rover—probably checking to see why she hadn't returned before this—and although she was pleased to see it, she couldn't quite suppress an anxiousness as to who was driving it. Was it Saxon, or one of his men? Oh, hell, how she hoped it was the latter!

But it wasn't, there was no mistaking just who was behind the wheel as he drew up in front of her, and she started to rub the palms of her hands down the sides of her slacks nervously. Leisurely he climbed down from the seat and, pushing his hands into the back pockets of fawn drill pants, paced slowly to where she was standing.

'Well?'

As she didn't think it was an enquiry after her health, Debra shifted uncomfortably beneath his enigmatic gaze and pointed down the slope. 'I'm sorry,' she offered contritely.

With his head inclined slightly to one side Saxon inspected the scene for what felt like an interminable length of time to his warily waiting companion. 'How did it happen?' he asked at last.

Very quiet, very controlled, and *very dangerous*! Debra shivered, and explained as concisely as possible.

'Of course you do realise you could have been killed!' Nowhere near as controlled now, and she sensed the final eruption wasn't far behind. 'So what the blazes were you doing driving that fast in the first place?'

'I wasn't d-driving *that* fast,' she stammered defensively.

'No? You always skid out of control when you brake, do you?'

'Of course not! But I couldn't see when the windshield broke.'

'And if you hadn't been going like a bat out of hell you wouldn't have needed to panic into slamming on the brakes!' he countered explosively. 'What if you'd had Prue with you? Have you thought of that?'

'I don't need to! If I'd had her with me it wouldn't have happened!' she retaliated without thinking.

'Oh? And why not?'

Debra's heart sank and her eyes closed in dismay. 'Because I wouldn't have been driving that fast,' she had no option but to confess, and thereby convict herself, as least as far as he was concerned.

'Exactly!' He nodded sarcastically, then caught hold of her arm with lean biting fingers. 'Well, let's go down and see what damage you've managed to cause.' His magnetic blue eyes slanted tauntingly over her. 'It could take you years to pay off all your debts to Wyeera.'

Seething resentment gave her the strength to break loose from his grasp and she glared at him rebelliously. 'You can look at it on your own, damn you!' she blazed. 'That's all you're worried about, your precious ute. Not once have you even asked how *I* am. How do you know I wasn't knocked unconscious going down there?'

'On what?'

That took some of the steam out of her, and she fixed him with a puzzled frown. 'What do you mean ... on what?'

He didn't immediately explain, but probed instead, 'You were wearing your seatbelt, weren't you?'

'Yes, but ...'

'Then as the car obviously hasn't rolled, it's extremely unlikely you would have hit your head on anything,' mockingly.

All Debra's fury returned in full force and with an incensed exclamation she swung a hand wildly at him, missed, and might have fallen down the bank as she lost her footing, had not a muscular arm gripped her securely about the waist. With her back pressed tightly against his side and that iron band about her midriff she was carried, fuming and struggling, all the way to the bottom.

'A word of warning, young lady,' Saxon bent to caution before letting her go, and with just enough steel in his voice for her to heed—albeit reluctantly. 'I already feel like giving you the hiding of your life, so if I were you I wouldn't provoke me too deliberately or you might yet find yourself unable to sit for a week!'

Permitting herself one long glance of smouldering mutiny, Debra flounced resentfully over to the ute. She would dearly like to have challenged that arrogant intimidation of his, but, she frustratingly had to admit, she just wasn't reckless enough to tempt fate to such a degree. Saxon McAllister wasn't the type given to making idle threats!

On following her, he took closer stock of the damage and then exhaled heavily. 'Well, I guess the first thing is to get it back up on to the road,' he declared ironically.

'How?' The question was out before she could prevent it. She had meant to keep a haughty, disinterested silence.

'There's a winch on the front of the Range-Rover ... fortunately!'

At the suggestion of sarcasm in his tone she immediately turned away again, a disgruntled expression on her face, and refused to even look—let alone offer to help—as he moved the larger vehicle into position and proceeded to couple the steel cable to the ute's tow bar.

'You can steer while I operate the winch.'

Now she had to face him. 'Steer what? That?' She pointed to the ute in no little dismay. She wasn't very keen on being a passenger while he attempted to haul it up the slope.

He nodded, a goading smile shaping his firm mouth. 'Someone has to—that flat tire will tend to make it pull continually to one side otherwise—and who better to keep it coming straight than the person who put it down there in the first place, hmm?'

Debra stifled her resentment with difficulty and gave him back a look of mock sorrowfulness. 'As long as you're not expecting too professional a performance. I've never done anything like this before.'

'Meaning I should recall the way you reversed out of the garage the first day you took Prue to school, I suppose?' he countered aggravatingly.

Nettled to find herself back on the defensive again so quickly, she immediately lifted her head higher to excuse, 'I'd never driven this make of car before then!'

Saxon's eyes gleamed sardonically, his gaze pointed as he looked at the ute. 'And you don't appear to have improved with practice either, if you don't mind my saying so.'

She did mind, of course, but as she suspected she would only be inviting more sarcasms of a like nature if she attempted a repudiation, she merely pressed her lips together vexedly and shrugged with what she hoped was suitably snubbing indifference as she slid into the driver's seat.

His instructions given, Saxon made his way up to

the Range-Rover to start the winch and Debra waited, nervously expectant, to feel the cable beginning to take the strain. When it did the ute jerked slightly but refused to move, and after two more attempts she wasn't surprised to feel the tension slackened altogether, or to see her employer's lithe figure approaching down the incline. What did surprise her, however, was his action on reaching the vehicle.

Without saying a word he opened the door, placed one hand on the back of the seat for support and leant across her to survey the instrument panel. Then, with his mouth levelling in mute exasperation, he reached in and released the handbrake.

'It helps,' he turned his head to taunt acidly.

'I'm sorry, I—I forgot I'd put it on when—when I stopped,' she apologised flusteringly, and uncertain whether her nervousness was due to her own embarrassing carelessness, or to his unbalancing closeness in such a confined space. She felt at least ten degrees warmer than she had a few seconds ago.

He smiled wryly, catastrophically for Debra since she found it impossible to drag her eyes away, and chucked her irritatingly beneath the chin. 'Never mind, sweetheart, it's the type of negligence I should have anticipated from a woman driver.'

'And that's just the sort of unfounded remark *I* would expect from a male chauvinist like you!' she condemned indignantly, slapping his hand away.

'Is that so?' One eyebrow slanted whimsically upwards. 'Then perhaps you'd better take care in case I'm tempted to follow it with a typically male chauvinistic reaction as well.'

'Like what?' Her eyes dared to challenge his insolently.

When his fingers rested against her chin this time it wasn't to touch fleetingly, but to hold inescapably. 'Like this,' he advised arrogantly, and covered her lips with his own in a hard, but thoroughly proficient, kiss.

Coming as it did after almost a week of cold sarcasm the action caught Debra totally unprepared and for a moment she was trapped in a mindless limbo. But when she discovered him to be exacting a response she was far from willing to give she began struggling frantically. Futilely also, it seemed, since she wasn't allowed to go free until Saxon cared to liberate her.

'Don't you ever dare touch me again!' The blazing words burst forth angrily the minute she was able to demonstrate her feelings.

'So who's going to stop me?' His question was no less bitingly delivered and, as if to prove his point, he lowered his mouth to hers once more before she even had a chance of replying, or taking evasive action.

Whirled deeper and deeper into a maelstrom of emotion she wanted so desperately to deny, Debra hit out blindly against her tormentor who could turn her whole being upside down with such ease. Saxon promptly reciprocated by pinning her wrists to the back of the seat, effectively trapping her head between her own imprisoned hands, while his lips continued their relentless assault on her tumultuous senses unopposed.

Not until her defences had crumbled entirely and her lips parted on a wayward sigh of surrender did he finally see fit to release her, and then only slowly, after he had drawn from her the response he had imperiously been demanding.

Humiliated beyond belief by her treacherous feelings, Debra pretended to an equanimity she was far from experiencing. 'Now, if you've quite finished, do you think we could return to the immediate problem of getting the ute back on to the road?' she enquired gibingly. 'I have quite a number of things which need doing today ... for Eleanor as well as yourself.'

'Whatever you say, lady!' He unexpectedly touched one finger to his temple in a teasing, laughing deference to her wishes which immediately undid all her efforts to keep her emotions under control as it sent waves of tingling awareness racing throughout her nervous system. 'Provided, of course, I receive some help from you this time.'

She might have known he would have the last word, she decided discontentedly, watching his agile progress back to the Range-Rover. He might have assented to her request that they make short work of returning to the homestead, but probably only because that coincided with his desire once he had summarily proved she wasn't capable of enforcing any orders she might give him—concerning herself, or otherwise!

With no handbrake to offer resistance, the ensuing attempt to pull the ute up to the road met with greater success, and although Debra was on tenterhooks the whole time lest she do something else wrong, they eventually made it to the top without anything else untoward happening.

'So far, so good,' commented Saxon drily after he had rewound the winch cable, then frowned as he unlocked the tail-gate of the ute and noticed for the first time the battered and partially destroyed state of some of the groceries. Pushing them aside in order to get at the spare tire he threw a querying glance over one shoulder. 'What happened to these?'

'The back opened and they fell out on the way down.'

He dropped the tire on to the ground and retrieved the jack before turning to face her, his expression sardonic in the extreme. 'Then in future, it might be an idea if you make certain you've shut it properly before you leave town, mightn't it?'

'Oh, *I* didn't shut it at all. One of the *men* at the store did,' it gave her the greatest of pleasure to be able to retort complacently. So self-satisfiedly, in fact, that she was persuaded to go a little further and taunt, 'So what have you got to say about that?'

'Nothing particularly complimentary,' he returned in repressive tones, going down on his haunches beside the ripped tire and beginning to loosen the wheel nuts. 'I dislike carelessness in any shape or form ... male or female!'

Intrigued by the play of muscles beneath his drill shirt, Debra moved to stand slightly behind him. 'You being a model of meticulous attentiveness, I suppose?' she quipped daringly.

'I will be—to you—if you don't cut the riling interruptions, sweetheart,' he promised meaningfully.

She shrugged, but prudently stepped back a pace,

and proceeded to make patterns in the dust with the toe of her right sandal. 'You like to goad me all the time,' she complained moodily.

He continued with what he was doing. 'Mmm, but then I'm a male chauvinist pig, remember?'

'I didn't say you were a pig,' she protested swiftly.

Now he spared her another glance and his mouth had assumed a humorous curve. 'I thought that was automatically implied along with the other.'

Debra felt her denial may have been too quickly made and decided on a hasty retreat, leaving a somewhat mumbled, 'Not always,' floating behind her as she wandered around to the far side of the Range Rover, and pretending she had suddenly lost interest in watching him work.

She wasn't at all sure herself why she should have rushed to make such a protest on his behalf, but rather than dwell on it she sank down in the shade created by the vehicle's bulk with her back propped against the wheel and deliberately occupied her mind by making mental notes of the things she would need to take with her for the two days they would be at Stratheden.

Somewhere between toothpaste and cleansing cream she guessed she must have dozed off, because the next thing she was conscious of was of being lifted to her feet to the accompaniment of a wryly drawled,

'It's a great life for some! Maybe I should have made you change the tire, seeing it was your efforts which ruined it.'

Still a little drowsy, Debra put out a hand for support and connected with a solidly powerful forearm which she clung to unthinkingly. 'I would have thought just having to replace it was enough to exempt me from doing the work as well,' she pouted.

'As if you don't know damned well you're not expected to pay for it!' All trace of laziness disappeared from Saxon's voice as he resolutely removed himself from her reach.

'But—but you said ... at least, you insinuated I would have to,' she recalled perplexedly, and was startled by his abrupt change in manner as she blinked herself back to full awareness.

'Did I?' His tone was still rough. 'Well, perhaps I decided in the meantime that I would rather forgo the money so you wouldn't feel obliged to prolong your employment with us in order to repay it.'

'I see,' she acknowledged thickly, her ebony-lashed eyes dimming to an anguished purple as a despairing ache settled in the region of her heart.

It was so reminiscent of his first attempted payoff that she could only stare at him mutely. Apparently nothing at all had changed, and she had only been deceiving herself by believing that that one spark of remorse—or had it only been pity, after all? —shown during the previous Sunday's storm would have altered his desire to see the last of her.

As swiftly as it had arrived, Saxon's harshness seemed to evaporate and he rubbed a hand wearily around the back of his neck. 'Oh, for God's sake, just get in this and take it home, will you?' he sighed. 'I'll follow in the ute.'

Only her lack of experience with the Range Rover stopped her from obeying immediately. 'I—I'm more used to d-driving the ute,' she just had to point out, but tentatively.

'One wouldn't know it!' he snapped sarcastically. 'Besides which, I want to test it out to make sure nothing else has been damaged, so it would be appreciated if you would just do as you're told without wasting more time by standing here arguing about who's going to drive which vehicle!'

'Yes, *sir*!' she muttered through clenched teeth, and stormed around to the driver's side. He deliberately found fault with every word she ever uttered!

CHAPTER SEVEN

THE two days spent at Stratheden with Saxon might have been informative for Debra, but they could hardly have been described as pleasant. He was an able teacher, but amiable companion he was not! She didn't know why he should have been in such a particularly grim mood, but by the time Sunday morning arrived she was only too pleased to return to Wyeera where she had *some* opportunities to escape his forbidding presence.

Matters did improve to a slight degree as the following weeks slipped past into months and the sale came closer, but she had long since despaired of him ever completely accepting her as his secretary. He hadn't wanted her in the position from the very beginning and, evidently, there hadn't been a solitary thing she had said or done since that had made him want to change his mind. Some days she was convinced she was making headway, but then, almost as if he was putting a deliberate brake on himself, he would give her one of those shrewdly assessing glances of his and she would be back to square one again.

And, as if that wasn't enough, she was now positive his decision to take her with him to Stratheden had been, as she half suspected at the time, purely an excuse to prevent her from seeing Paul. Three times since he had done exactly the same thing—

with differing reasons on each occasion, of course!
—but it had become more than obvious to Debra that
he didn't intend for her to gain any more enjoyment
from her stay on the property than he could possibly
help. Only once had she managed an evening out
without his watchful company—Paul had taken her
to a party in town—but that had only come about
because Saxon had been in Brisbane at the time discussing the sale with his stock and station agents'
head office. Oh, he saw that she had adequate free
time, all right. The only trouble was, he also saw to
it that it never coincided with anyone else's, and certainly *never* when there was anything on in town that
he wasn't planning to attend!

She had even once gone so far as to accuse him of
being unable to differentiate between employment
and imprisonment, but that had only earned her his
stock reply to any complaint she might make of
always being able to resign if she didn't like the conditions, and she had had no choice but to let the matter drop.

Not only was she still reluctant to let him make
her resign, but she was also beginning to doubt now
whether she could resign. No matter what he thought
of her, she couldn't control her own headstrong emotions—or the direction in which they unerringly
headed—and it had taken very little soul-searching to
discover she had unwittingly, and definitely unwisely,
fallen in love with a man who not only didn't need
her—there was always tenacious Anthea to consider
—but who had made it all too apparent he didn't
want her either.

She supposed she was being foolish by deliberately refusing to leave but, right at the moment, she couldn't bear the thought that if she did go she would more than likely never see him again. For the time being, at least, she preferred to suffer his barbed remarks rather than not hear his voice at all. Besides, she managed to convince herself, if she did give in her notice now he might conceivably start delving for the reason behind her sudden capitulation, and his stinging comments, should he be successful, she simply didn't dare think about.

The afternoon prior to the sale, however, an incident occurred in Acacia Crossing which had Debra pondering her decision yet again, but a trifle fearfully this time. Saxon had been involved in a car accident, and although he had neither been in the wrong, nor hurt, her old anxieties had immediately returned to plague her the moment she heard about it. Perhaps she was only being stupidly superstitious, but no matter how hard she tried, she just couldn't dispel the thought that some people *did* seem to attract, or bring, far more bad luck than others. And that was the crux of her whole problem. Was she prepared to take the chance?

It was a question which kept her awake well into the night and, judging by the untidy state of the bedclothes next morning, hadn't been out of her mind even after she had finally fallen asleep. But, by the time she went down to breakfast, she did have her answer. All things considered, no, she wasn't prepared to take that chance!

Naturally enough the talk at the table that morning concentrated on the sale, but apart from a couple of vague acknowledgments to queries directly put to her, Debra added very little to the conversation. She was mentally composing a letter of resignation. And afterwards, she still wasn't able to get to the office because it was a Friday and Prue had to be driven to school—much to her disgust at having to miss out on what she obviously considered the most exciting day of her visit.

The return trip seemed to take hours longer than normal to Debra, although in actual time spent on the road it didn't, but she did meet considerably more traffic on her way as a steady stream of prospective buyers headed for the property. Most of them, she knew from enquiries they had received during the preceding weeks, would be coming by air. In fact, two plane loads had already arrived before she left with Prue, and it wasn't difficult to surmise that after the sale ring the airstrip would probably be the most used area of Wyeera that day.

From the garages she could just make out Saxon's commanding figure as he stood talking to Neale and Mike down by the cattle yards and she hurriedly slipped across to the homestead and into the office. Maybe it was because she really didn't want to write the letter, but it took her an unreasonable amount of time to eventually settle on three suitable lines which would sever her association with Saxon McAllister for good. When it was finished she put her signature to it quickly, slipped it into an envelope and, taking the coward's way out, laid it on his desk. Once she had found the courage to write it, there just wasn't any left over to enable her to hand it to him personally.

On her way outside once more she met Jeanne and

her mother crossing the verandah with their arms filled with food containers. The Ladies' Auxiliary was doing the catering again.

'I suppose you're excused kitchen duty for today?' grinned Jeanne ruefully as, with a smile, Debra stepped back to allow them to pass.

'Mmm, I think so. I'm just off to the yards now to see if I'm needed.'

'Ah well, I'll think of you out there in all that dust and heat while I'm slicing tomatoes, etcetera, in Eleanor's nice air-conditioned kitchen.'

'Thanks!' Debra laughed ruefully herself now. 'That really makes me look forward to it.'

'Pay her no mind, Debra,' Mrs Bartlett counselled over her shoulder as she disappeared down the hall. 'You know what a curse jealousy is.'

Winking at the girl beside her, Jeanne began following her parent. 'Well, it is *my* fiancé who's working down there, Mother,' she pointed out with humorous emphasis.

What Mrs Bartlett had to say in reply to that Debra couldn't hear and she continued on her way with a smile tugging at her soft lips. The Bartletts were a nice friendly family.

The usual inspection of cattle prior to sale was under way when she reached the yards, and with such a sizeable throng of men around it took her quite some time to locate Saxon in front of the bull pens inside one of the outbuildings where he and two other men were discussing the merits of one of Wyeera's finest animals. Uncertain whether to interrupt them or not, Debra hovered hesitantly near the adjoining pen for a few minutes until Neale arrived with another group, whereupon she gave a wry apology for being in the way and, taking one last look at her employer, found him holding out an arm towards her.

He was answering a question when she made it to his side, after skirting another quartet coming from the opposite direction, and couldn't help darting him a glance of wide-eyed surprise when that outstretched arm was draped across her shoulders to pull her protectively close and shield her against the press of the ever-increasing crowd.

A swift introduction to his two companions when he had concluded what he was saying and then he was lowering his head to ask, 'What can I do for you?'

Disastrously aware of him as never before, as she was, it was all she could do to reply. 'I—er—came to ask what you wanted *me* to do,' she managed finally in something of a husky whisper.

'I'm sorry?' He bent his head even closer, his forehead furrowing. 'There's too much noise in here. I couldn't hear you.'

To make sure he heard it this time Debra went up on her toes in order to close the gap even further, but as she did so someone bumped into her from behind and caused her lips to graze across his cheek. For a split second her selfconscious gaze locked with a glittering blue one and the air was electric between them. Then, with a gulp, and a mumbled, 'I'm sorry,' she sank down to her normal height again.

'That's as may be.' Unexpectedly, white teeth gleamed in a tantalising smile. 'But you still haven't told me what you came for.'

'Oh!' She flushed embarrassedly and tore her be-mused eyes away. 'It was only to—only to see what you wanted me to do.'

'Well . . .' His head tilted consideringly. 'You could give Mike a hand once the bidding starts. He'll probably be wanting some help with the buyers' instruction sheets to make sure they're filled in correctly, and legibly. Sometimes they can be rather difficult to read when they've been filled in against a fence post or someone else's back, and you probably know the Lot numbers as well as anyone by now.'

That was the truth! She had certainly been through them often enough since that first time she had taken all their particulars down from the computer.

'Anything else?' Her finely marked brows peaked quizzically.

His expression was dry as he looked up and down the packed walkway between the two rows of pens. 'Apart from the fact that it would appear it's impossible for you to squeeze your way out of here at the moment in order to carry out any instructions I might give, no, I don't think so.'

As much as she was inclined to agree with him regarding her chances of getting through the crowd, she still thought it preferable to at least try rather than stay where she was.

'Oh, I'll manage somehow,' she smiled blithely, and made a move to leave.

Saxon's grip tightened spontaneously. 'And I think not,' he countermanded blandly.

Unless she wanted to make herself look extremely foolish by fighting to get away it seemed she had little option but to accept his ultimatum with as much grace as possible and, with a defeated sigh, she reluctantly consented to remain where she was. No doubt he was probably only calling a truce while there were visitors around—as had always been his custom—but whether that was for her benefit, or his, she hadn't yet been able to decide.

In an attempt to distract her thoughts from such personal considerations Debra listened intently to the men's conversation as they progressed very slowly along the pens, and was privately quite proud when she realised she also had a very good idea of the points they were looking for in each beast they stopped to inspect, thanks to Saxon's expert tuition. And once, almost as much to her own surprise as theirs, she was even able to make a knowledgeable comparison between the two bloodlines they happened to be discussing at the time.

'Well, it sounds as if you've picked yourself a secretary who's got a memory for pedigrees this time, Mac,' applauded the taller of his two associates.

'Which is something that couldn't be said of your last one,' added the other.

Debra didn't say anything. She was too occupied in digesting the information that her predecessor apparently hadn't been the paragon in all respects that she had been led to believe after all.

'Oh, yes, Debra's very good when it comes to identifying the different strains.'

If she hadn't been able to feel his hand so definitely through the lightweight material of her pink slacks suit Debra would have sworn she was dreaming.

Surely that wasn't Saxon *praising* something she'd done!

As a result, when their two companions moved slightly ahead, she couldn't resist sending the man beside her a glowering look and mouthing accusingly, 'I thought you said Noreen was the whizz kid of all time with the stud records!'

'And so she was ... while she was working with the computer,' he admitted drily. 'Unfortunately, the minute you took her away from it she couldn't remember one bloodline from the other.'

There were quite a number of gibes she could have come back with regarding that convenient omission, but in the end she decided against all of them. With her resignation already lying on his desk there didn't seem much point in raking up old grievances, or starting new ones.

He evidently had been expecting one, though, for when it didn't eventuate he promptly slanted her a keenly measuring glance which had her rushing to divert his attention by nodding her head towards the two men ahead of them and advising, 'They're waiting for you.'

At last they made it to the end of the building and Debra could escape. But not before Saxon had managed to put a scare into her.

'Have you given Mike all the necessary vaccination certificates?' he asked.

'No, not yet.' She shook her head. 'I'll get them for him now.'

'Don't bother,' her offer was waved aside negligently. 'I'll do it myself. I want to have a word with him about them, anyway.'

'It's no bother!' She was already on her way as she said it. The last thing she wanted was for him to discover her resignation this early in the day. 'I want to get a pen and notepad from the office. I think I might have need of them if I'm going to be helping Mike.'

As it turned out, once the auction began she had never spoken a truer word. There were requests to be noted, enquiries which needed following up, and a host of other details she would never have remembered if she hadn't been able to write them down. Also, she had to check the instruction sheets as they came in after each Lot was knocked down, and often it would be a case of her having to chase after a particular buyer in order to remind, 'Excuse me, but you haven't stated what feed and bedding is required on the journey,' or, 'I'm sorry, but you haven't said where you wish your purchases consigned to. Are they to go to your home address?'

It was after one of these forays into the crowd that she found Neale beckoning to her urgently as she passed the walkway which led to the sale ring on her return to the auctioneers' stand. On either side of him stood enormous hump-backed bulls with leather halters about their heads which he was grasping firmly.

'Be a love and take this one into the ring for me,' he smiled persuasively, and held out one of the leads as she put her head between two of the rails to eye him enquiringly.

'M-m-*me*? She stared back at him, horrified.

'He's as quiet as a lamb,' he assured her earnestly.

'But where are the men? Where's Saxon?' There

had been plenty of them around when she left.

'Down the back.' He nodded behind him. 'One of the stupid ...' He coughed politely and started again. 'One of the bulls has managed to lock his horns in the steel gate.'

'But surely there's *someone*!' glancing up and down the walkway hopefully.

'Just you, at the moment,' he grinned.

'Neale!' she wailed plaintively, then reluctantly climbed through the bars when she sensed no help would be forthcoming. 'What if he runs amok, or something? I always thought Brahmans weren't a particularly biddable breed.'

'I promise you, he's used to being handled. He's stud, not commercial.'

Debra eyed the young grey giant who literally towered over her askance. 'Does *he* know that?' she quipped drily.

'Would I ask you to take him if I thought he'd give you any trouble?' he countered plausibly, handing over the relevant halter into her somewhat lax fingers. Besides,' a broad grin made its appearance, 'with that many men outside the ring I'm sure he'd only have to look sideways at you to have half of them over the fence and offering to help out.'

'I wouldn't complain if they did that now,' Debra grimaced wryly before giving a tug to her charge and sighing, 'Oh, come on then, you great lump! Put your best foot forward and let's get this over and done with as soon as possible. But so help me, if you so much as breathe on me,' she squinted up at him mock threateningly, 'I'll belt you one on the nose with my notebook!'

Fortunately, there was no call for her threat to be put into practice—not that it would have been a deterrent in any case, as she well knew—although she did have to lean her shoulder into the animal a couple of times, as she had seen the men do, in order to make him turn when and where she wanted. The bidding rose quickly, as she had guessed it would as soon as the auctioneer called out his name and pedigree, but it did seem to take a long time before the final price was reached and she could return to the walkway in relief.

The men had also reappeared by then and she was met by a barrage of wide smiles as she handed over her charge with far more enthusiasm than when she had accepted him.

'A very experienced showing,' drawled Saxon as she came abreast of him, and received a very expressive grimace in return, but which was just as obviously meant for all of them.

'I'll say!' laughed one of the grooms. 'Did you hear the price he reached?'

'I heard,' with evident satisfaction.

'You don't reckon it could have been a case of them being too busy watching the handler to realise what they were bidding?' Neale grinned as he prepared to move into the ring in his turn.

'Could be,' Saxon conceded, his eyes gliding lazily over Debra. 'We'll just have to give her another one to lead around for us to find out, won't we?'

'Like fun!' she retorted explicitly, and scrambled out through the rails before she could be inveigled into anything else. 'You may all have found it amusing, but I'll have you know,' her lips swept upwards into a delightfully rueful smile, '*I* hate the lot of you!'

Their following laughter brought forth many an interested look, but Debra left it to them to do any enlightening, if they cared to, while she continued back to her seat beside Mike, where she made certain she stayed for the rest of the morning.

Lunch was a convivial meal served smorgasbord style on the verandah, and after helping to see that the visitors were all catered for, Debra took hers with Eleanor, Mrs Bartlett, and Jeanne. Not that they were granted much time for conversation because, all too soon, everyone was resuming their places and, with a smiled apology for her companions, she prepared to do likewise.

On her way to her bedroom to renew her lipstick she met Saxon coming from the other direction, and the absolutely livid set of his features immediately informed her that he was in the foulest mood imaginable. Without having heard that anything had gone wrong she naturally wondered at the cause, and no one could have been more astonished than she was when a ruthless hand snaked out to grip her wrist painfully as their paths crossed.

'*You're* just the one I want!' he ground out explosively as, without a word of explanation, he spun about and began dragging her along behind him.

Debra's brain raced chaotically. What had she done now? Left something important out of the brochure? Put something in that she shouldn't have? Given the wrong advice to someone? She shook her head dismissively. She really couldn't think of a thing that would generate this amount of wrath!

He turned into the office and she was thrust un-

ceremoniously into the room while he slammed the
door shut with a crash she felt sure must have been
heard all the way to the sale ring, and then stalked
towards his desk.

'And just what the bloody hell's the meaning of
this?' He slapped a hand down furiously on to her
opened letter of resignation.

Dumbfounded, she could only stand and stare at
him in round-eyed amazement. Jubilation, mockery,
sarcasm, taunts—those she had all expected—but not
anger! She swallowed nervously and gave a slight
shrug. 'It's my resignation.'

'I'm well aware of what it is!' he lashed back savagely. 'I asked the meaning for it!'

'Isn't it enough that you've got it?' she evaded
tautly.

'No! I want to know *why*!'

With every tense inch of her showing defiance she
held his brilliant gaze stoutly. 'Because you've won.
Why else?'

'Oh, don't give me that!' His voice changed to one
of contemptuous disgust. 'Only two days ago you
were reiterating your denial that I could make you
leave, and as I was away for most of yesterday and
hardly said more than a dozen words to you all day,
kindly don't play me for a credulous idiot by expecting me to believe any of your, "Because you've won",
myths!'

'And that's just what this is all about, isn't it?' she
was goaded into taunting. 'You're just infuriated
because it wasn't due to *your* efforts that I resigned!'

'Not at all,' he repudiated the suggestion tersely.
'Because until I'm satisfied with the reason, I shall

simply refuse to accept it,' as he deliberately tore the typewritten page into pieces and dropped them into the waste basket.

Debra watched the last of them flutter out of sight and then put a hand dazedly to her head. 'You can't do that,' she protested.

'I just did!'

'Then I'll write out another one.'

'Don't waste your time!'

'You're just being perverse!' Her voice rose angrily.

'Am I?' A long-legged stride brought him menacingly closer. 'I would have said it was the other way around!'

'Oh, I wouldn't doubt for a minute that's what you'd say,' she gibed. 'You're so . . .'

A knock on the door interrupted her and it was Neale who put his head apologetically into the room in response to Saxon's acknowledgment to advise, 'Sorry, Mac, but I thought you'd want to know we're ready to start again.'

'Thanks, Neale, I'm coming.' And to Debra in a peremptory tone as he headed after his manager, 'We'll finish this later.'

'There's nothing to finish,' she contradicted with a pert lift of her chin. 'I don't have to discuss my reasons for wanting to leave with you.'

'But you will!'

'I will not!' It was a mutinous mutter rather than a confident refusal, although in either case it was doubtful if Saxon heard, because he was already making his way down the hall.

Debra continued on to her bedroom more slowly,

her thoughts understandably confused. She had been preparing herself for sarcastic elation, not an irate explosion, and she just couldn't fathom why he should apparently care what had prompted her to hand in her notice. She would have thought he would have been only too happy to see her go, for whatever reason! Or maybe, no matter what he said to the contrary, it was as she had first suggested. Saxon just wasn't used to being thwarted, and the knowledge that all his efforts had failed to achieve the desired result was what had really riled him.

A theory which, unfortunately, didn't make Debra feel any better, for whenever her eyes happened to collide with his still smouldering gaze during the afternoon session of the sale, she was promptly reminded of his parting remarks and shivers of apprehension would begin trickling down her spine at the thought of what might yet be to come. Having succeeded in foiling him once, she knew without a doubt that it was going to be doubly hard to repeat the performance.

'What happened to you at lunchtime?' Mike's amused-sounding question brought her out of one of her many periods of introspection with a start.

'Oh—er—nothing in particular,' she prevaricated lightly. 'What makes you ask?'

'Only the fact that it's been perfectly obvious your mind's been anywhere but on the sale since we returned,' he enlightened her in extremely dry tones.

'I'm very sorry,' she smiled at him penitently. 'Have I missed anything?'

'Just Mac's signals to you over the last five minutes.'

She pulled a dismayed face and glanced over to where Saxon stood beside the gate leading into the ring, his exasperated expression being directed straight at her.

'Oh, hell, I'd better get over there and see what he wants. Why didn't you say something before?' she queried as she pushed out of her chair.

'I tried, in between bids,' he divulged with a laugh. 'But you ignored me too.'

'Then I guess I'd better apologise for that too.' Her smile was ruefully shaped. 'It would appear my concentration has been sadly lacking this afternoon.'

'No worries. There hasn't been anything that needed it so far.'

Except for Saxon's summons, of course, Debra mused sardonically as she made her way round to the gate.

'So you finally managed to stir yourself into coming?' he greeted her with a sarcastic inflection to his voice.

She supposed she deserved that. 'I'm sorry. I wasn't aware you wanted me until Mike told me.'

'Perhaps, if you'd been paying attention, you wouldn't have needed to wait for him to tell you.'

'I guess not,' she accepted his stricture with a sigh. 'But I'm here now.'

'Too late, unhappily!' he snapped.

'Oh?' Her brows drew together in a frown. 'For what?'

'For collecting Prue earlier than usual,' he informed her coldly. 'I've had to send someone else instead.'

'I don't see why!' she fired resentfully. 'I knew

Prue wanted to get home as soon as possible this afternoon and, according to my calculations, I still had
another ten minutes or so before I needed to leave.'

'Mmm, but by the way you were day-dreaming up
there I couldn't be sure you'd remember at all.' His
retort was satirically goading. 'In addition to which,
Eleanor wanted a parcel of bulbs picked up from
Simpson's beforehand.'

'She didn't mention anything about it to me,' suspiciously.

'No? Well, maybe she couldn't attract your attention either!'

Before Debra had a chance to deal with that gibing attack another voice came from close by, a voice
dripping with false concern.

'Oh, dear, have we arrived at an inappropriate
time? You don't sound very pleased with your secretary today, Mac,' Anthea smiled up at him archly.

Her companion was Paul, who Debra greeted
warmly, even as she listened for Saxon's reply.

'How could I not be?' he counter-questioned
smoothly, if a little ironically, in Debra's estimation.
'She paraded one of our top money-earners in the
ring this morning.'

'Good on you!' Paul applauded with a grin.
Anthea, as was to be expected, was far less complimentary.

'You didn't!' she exclaimed, pretending to be im-
pressed, and then gave a coy laugh. 'Of course, I'm
not big enough or strong enough to control one of
those great beasts. I just wouldn't know what to do
if they decided to misbehave.'

'Oh, a threatened belting with a notebook seems to

work wonders,' advised Debra drily. The other girl was at it again! Apparently she was to be labelled as King Kong's stand-in this time. 'Once they've realised what damage you can do with one of those, they're no trouble at all.'

'Now you're teasing me,' Anthea protested with a girlish pout, and turned to the man beside her for confirmation, saying, 'She is, isn't she, Mac?'

'I wouldn't know.' Saxon hunched wide shoulders dispassionately, although his mouth took on an amused twist, but further than that he refused to comment, going on instead to ask, 'What brings you out here, anyway, Anthea?'

'Oh, I met Paul while I was in town, so when he said he intended coming out to see how things were progressing I invited myself along too. I thought you might offer to drive me home again afterwards,' she smiled up at him with an overweening confidence which stabbed at Debra excruciatingly.

'Not tonight, I'm sorry,' he appeared to have no hesitation in declining her blatant encouragement. 'Apart from the fact that some of these,' motioning towards the men clustered about the ring, 'won't be leaving until well into the evening, I also have other pressing matters to attend to tonight,' as his eyes clashed purposefully with Debra's above the shorter girl's head.

'That's all right, I don't mind waiting for you,' Anthea persisted. 'I'm sure Eleanor won't object to one extra for dinner.'

'You're welcome to stay for dinner, of course,' Saxon allowed courteously, but in a voice which had tightened so markedly that Debra found herself

cringing inwardly on the other girl's behalf. 'And I
shall be only too pleased ...'

'I knew you'd eventually agree,' the brunette interrupted with a victorious smirk, and had at least two
of her listeners staring at her in disbelief for her in-
sensitivity.

'... to ensure you have someone to escort you home
... but it will not be me!' Saxon continued as if she
had never spoken. 'I will be otherwise occupied!'

Suddenly, as his words penetrated, a hectic red
stain splashed over Anthea's cheeks and her eyes
glittered spitefully. 'With *her*?' she went so far as to
forget herself and snap.

There was no necessity for anyone to ask for
clarification. They all knew exactly who she meant,
and while Paul promptly uttered a disgusted snort at
the outspoken accusation, Debra could only stand
by stiffly and feel the tint of selfconscious colour
surging into her own face.

Saxon was nowhere near as forbearing, however,
as with an imperious wave of his hand he brought
one of his men over. 'Miss Devenish wishes to leave,
Charley,' he advised icily. 'Would you take her home
in the station wagon, please?'

It was the ultimate snub. He was turning her off the
property, and without even giving her the satisfaction
of an answer. And Anthea, unwilling to have her
pride lacerated in front of one of the stockmen as
well, had no option but to accept the rebuff with as
much control as possible.

As soon as she had left Debra smiled nervously
and prepared to make her departure too. 'If you'll
excuse me, I'd better get back and see if Mike has

anything he wants me to do,' she said.

'Hey!' Paul reached out a hand to prevent her moving. 'It wasn't only to see how the sale was going that I came out here, you know.'

Indecision was written all over her face as she looked from one of them to the other, and it was Saxon who did her replying for her, his tone still a little taut. 'Sorry, old son, but you'll have to wait, I'm afraid. Debra has work to do at the moment.'

Paul laughed wryly, his eyes turning skywards. 'I know, business before pleasure!' he quoted.

Actually, Debra had so many things to think about that she wasn't unhappy to escape from both of them. Saxon, because the less she saw of him from now on the better it would be for her peace of mind, and Paul, because although she liked him, that was all she felt for him, and she didn't want to give him any ideas to the contrary.

CHAPTER EIGHT

As Saxon had prophesied, certainly not all the visitors left when the sale was concluded, and dinner was over and the evening well advanced by the time the last of them had finished partaking of their host's hospitality and departed. For Debra's part, she was sorry to see them go, conscious as she had been of a deliberating gaze resting on her the whole time they had been toasting the success of the sale, both from the sellers' and the buyers' points of view.

Now, as the final set of red tail-lights disappeared down the road to the main gate, she decided it was time to make herself scarce and, surmising her bedroom would offer no sanctuary against someone of Saxon's determination, she stayed only long enough to strip off her slacks suit and don a pair of jeans and an old cotton shirt, then headed outdoors. Perhaps, she hoped, on finding her room empty, Saxon would save his interrogation for another day. A day when she felt a little more prepared to endure it than she did right at the moment.

For the first half hour or so she wandered around aimlessly, up to the sleep-out on the roof, around Eleanor's bush houses, and then down towards the outbuildings. The air was pleasantly cool against her skin, but as she came round the corner of the cattle shed where she had found Saxon earlier that morning she caught the full force of the breeze, and to elude the cold draught she slipped inside.

It was quiet now, the dimmed light overhead show-ing most of the animals to be asleep, and completely unaware that within a few days they would be start-ing journeys—extremely long ones in some instances —to new homes. Slowly she made her way down the pens on the right-hand side, trying to recall the pedi-gree of each occupant as she passed, and then turned and started back up the other row. As she neared the end some sixth sense made her look towards the doorway and, with a sharply inhaled breath, she came to a standstill.

Saxon seemed to fill the opening as he stood there indolently with his hands resting on lean hips, and how long he had been there she had no way of know-ing. He had changed too, she noted, from the mole-skins and white shirt he had been wearing all day to slim-fitting jeans and a denim shirt which gave him such an earthy, untrammelled air that she closed her eyes in despair. Oh, God, why did he have to look so invincible, so hypnotising, so damned flag-rantly male?

'You've led me quite a chase,' he drawled wryly as long easy strides shortened the distance between them.

'Oh?' She smiled weakly and pushed her hands into the pockets of her jeans in an effort to imitate his self-assuredness. 'I didn't realise you were look-ing for me.'

His lips twitched and then stilled. 'Well, I guess it doesn't matter now that I've found you, does it?'

'I suppose not,' she shrugged, and flattened herself against the steel rails of the pen beside her in the hope of stepping around him. 'Although it is getting late, and—and ...' She stopped with a jerk as a bronzed hand slapped down on to the rail just in front of her.

'But not too late for us to complete our discussion, I trust?'

A quick duck under that restricting arm and she was edging towards the door with her back pressed against the rail. 'Discussion?' she echoed innocently.

As he kept pace with her a knowing glint appeared in the depths of his blue eyes. 'You'll never make it, you know.'

She certainly wouldn't if she didn't try! 'I don't know what you're talking about,' she parried.

'You're trying to play me for a fool again, sweetheart.' Saxon stroked one forefinger warningly across her burning cheek.

Debra began moving faster. 'Not me, boss,' she quipped flippantly.

'Yes, *you*, you little witch!' Her progress was abruptly halted by two hands descending on to the rail this time, one on either side of her, and he leant disturbingly close to propose, 'So let's go back to the beginning, shall we?'

'The beginning of what?' she desperately denied knowledge of his meaning.

'Debra!' One hand left the rail in order to span her jaw. 'Believe me, one way or another, I mean to discover why you suddenly decided to resign.'

'It's none of your business!'

'I happen to think otherwise.'

'And once again you're *wrong*!' Anger was her last resort and she used it unstintingly. 'The same as you've been wrong in every single thought you've ever had about me. You've accused me of everything unpleasant you could think of, done all you possibly could to make my life unbearable, and now you want to add browbeating to your list!' She glared at him fiercely, her breath coming in shallow gasps. 'Well, I've got news for you, Saxon McAllister! This is one time you're not having everything your own way!'

'The hell it's not!'

His lips came down on hers hard and determinedly, and against this new attack she had no defence whatsoever. Anger was of little use to her now—his actions too closely paralleled her own wayward desires—and as her heart swiftly took control from her head she melted against him uninhibitedly, her pliant form moulding itself to his rugged length and delighting in the pressure of strong arms which ensured she couldn't stray.

When it became clear she had no intention of fighting him the autocratic demands of his mouth changed to leisurely, persuasive caresses which drugged her mind to the exclusion of all else and had her ardently seeking more. With a deep-throated groan Saxon suddenly bent to swing her off her feet and into his arms, carrying her with sure steps to an empty stall used for storage, and sinking down with her among the piles of fresh clean straw.

Debra's half closed eyes were a deep, drowsy purple as she reached up to entwine slim arms about his neck and draw his head down to hers again, her gently parted lips an invitation impossible to ignore. Beneath her exploring fingers she could feel the sinewed slope of his shoulders and, remembering a night when she had been able to touch that tanned skin unobstructed, she shyly began unfastening his shirt. A convulsive shudder shook him at her first tentative contact and he gathered her ever closer, even as his lips played havoc with the pulsing nerve at the side of her throat.

Her senses were on fire and she could feel swift fingers efficiently removing the barrier of her shirt and bra, but she made no move to resist. She loved him more than he would ever know and when he made her feel like this she could deny him nothing. Nevertheless, when a work-hardened hand slid upwards to cup a firm, swelling breast she couldn't restrain the quiver of raw emotion which surged through her, a tremor which quickly became a raging flood as warm lips followed to tease an already aroused nipple into throbbing ecstasy.

For a moment she thought her heart would burst, so hard was it beating, and then in the next breath believed it had stopped altogether, from shock, when Saxon lifted his head to pin her with an impassioned blue gaze and groaned thickly,

'Dear God! When are you going to marry me?'

It was the last thing she had expected, but what she wanted most, and it was only by drawing on the very last reserves of her willpower that she managed to shake her head weakly.

'I'm not,' she whispered brokenly.

His eyes searched hers questioningly, deeply. 'In the name of heaven, why not? You must know by now how much I love you, and I'm damned sure you're not exactly uninterested in me either!'

Embarrassed by her nakedness now, Debra rolled to her knees and away from him as she hastily refastened her clothes. 'I just can't, that's all,' she choked, head downbent.

'Don't you think I'm at least entitled to know why?' A gentle hand swept her tousled hair aside in order to rest lightly against the nape of her neck.

If anything her head drooped even lower, but she didn't answer.

'Is it because you don't love me?' he probed.

Again she didn't answer and he continued, 'Then is it because you don't think I love you?'

The merest movement of her head negated that supposition and for a few seconds there was utter silence. Then, in a keenly perceptive tone, he enquired suspiciously, 'This doesn't happen to have anything to do with the reason you resigned, does it?'

He was too close for comfort and she shook her head vigorously this time, and was amazed to hear a briefly mocking laugh sound behind her. Confused, she half turned to look at him and found him beckoning to her. When she refused to comply he simply caught her about the waist and pulled her around to face him.

'As delightful as your back might be, it's your face I'm interested in seeing at the moment, sweetheart,' he advised wryly.

'So you can laugh at me again?' stiffly.

'Laugh at you? I could beat you for what you're doing to me!' His voice deepened hoarsely. 'That laugh you heard was directed at myself for having let a violet-eyed witch turn my well-ordered life into a shambles, and for being driven half out of my mind because she won't tell me why she wants to take herself out of it again!'

'Oh, Saxon.' She stared at him helplessly, tears welling into her eyes. 'It's only because I love you so much that I have to leave.'

A mirthless smile caught at his lips. 'If you'll pardon me for saying so, that may sound very touching, but it offers little comfort.'

'You don't believe me?'

'I don't know what to believe any more! You've got my thoughts almost as tangled as yours, and I'm ...' He broke off abruptly to exclaim in dawning comprehension, 'Good God Almighty! That just goes to prove what you've done to my thought processes or I would have realised long ago. I knew *I* couldn't make you resign—I think I was subconsciously counting on it, in fact—but what I didn't allow for was a superstitious little idiot who unbelievably considers herself to be some sort of jinx.' He leant forward to cup her face between his hands and query softly, 'That's it, isn't it, Debra?'

There was no call for her to agree, the answer was in her misty eyes, although she still had to convince him, 'And that's exactly why I can't stay.'

'You might just as well, because now I know the reason, wherever you go I'll be right there behind you,' he promised. 'My days of pretending I can live without you are over.'

He couldn't be serious! 'But—but what about all this?' She spread one hand expressively wide.

'Neale's a good manager.'

'It's your whole life!'

'Uh-uh!' He shook his head decisively. '*You*'re my whole life.'

How could she keep fighting when everything in her wanted to surrender? 'But I'd die if something happened to you because of me,' she cried tremulously.

'I wouldn't be too keen on it myself,' he grinned drily, and bent to kiss the tears from her flushed cheeks.

'Oh, please don't joke about it,' she begged. 'It really frightens me.'

Saxon drew her trembling figure to him tenderly, his eyes the softest blue she had ever seen them. 'I know, sweetheart, I know,' he soothed. 'But that's what I'm here for, remember? To make sure nothing ever frightens you again.'

His confidence was reassuring and she did so *want* to believe. 'You think I'm being foolish, don't you?' she tilted her face ruefully up to his.

It was too good an opportunity to miss and his lips closed over hers satisfyingly. 'I think I'm very fortunate to have found someone who cares so deeply,' he breathed unevenly long moments later.

'You still haven't answered my question, though.'

He sighed and held her slightly away from him. 'What can I say? You already know my feelings with regard to luck, good or bad. Although there is one aspect of this I feel perhaps should be pointed out to you.'

'Which is?'

'That your natural parents' deaths had nothing whatsoever to do with luck! I'm afraid they brought it on themselves by failing to wear life-jackets. You survived because you were wearing one, and there's no reason to suppose they wouldn't have done so too if they'd taken the proper precautions.'

'I guess I've never really thought of it in that light before,' she mused pensively. 'Although you couldn't say that about Rose and Jack Armitage.'

'No, theirs was a case of pure bad luck,' he acceded with a shrug. 'But freak accidents do happen at times and, in this case, I rather think the blame could more appropriately be laid at Mother Nature's door than yours.'

He made it sound all so logical. 'And Jay, the boy at the orphanage?' she couldn't help asking.

Recognising her need to be convinced, he smiled wryly and reasoned, 'Darling, as distressing a fact as it may be, children have been getting themselves killed by running out on to roads from behind buses, cars, carriages, and anything else you like to name, ever since man first devised means of transport for himself, but I hardly think it's fair to suggest you were the cause of it all.'

'There's your accident yesterday too, don't forget.'

'And if all car accidents were that innocuous we would all consider ourselves fortunate!' he countered swiftly. 'You had more chance of injuring yourself when you drove over the embankment.'

'I didn't *drive* over,' she was diverted into protesting indignantly. 'It just sort of ... slid over.'

'Yes, well, that's what the driver's supposed to be there for, you know. To prevent that from happening,' he teased.

She knew he was only doing it to stop her thoughts

returning to less pleasant subjects, but he needn't have worried. Although he might not have yet completely laid to rest every last one of her doubts—they had been with her too long to be dismissed altogether that quickly—at least he had done the next best thing by bringing them back into perspective. Now, with her head tilting to one side, she cast him a provocative look from beneath luxuriant lashes.

'If I asked you to hold me, would you accuse me of propositioning you?' she quizzed banteringly.

'No,' he laughed in recognition of the phrase. 'But then, once again, I couldn't guarantee that's all I'd do either.'

Debra pressed closer and wound her arms adoringly about his neck. 'I'm willing to take the chance if you are,' she murmured throatily, her surrender complete.

'Oh, God yes!' His arms crushed her to him possessively, his mouth hungrily accepting all that she voluntarily offered. 'I love you so much it hurts!'

For Debra, he was her every dream come true, and had he asked it of her she would have given herself to him there and then. She had no reservations where he was concerned. But he didn't ask, he pulled reluctanly away instead.

'When *are* you going to marry me, sweetheart?' he repeated his original questioning fervently.

Even white teeth shone in a smile of bewitching radiance. 'Whenever you want.'

'It can't be soon enough for my liking,' he owned expressively. 'I've wanted you for a long, long time now.' A long forefinger followed the outline of her lips delicately. 'And the night of that damned storm was nearly my undoing. My God, I went in to comfort you, but if I'd stayed any longer I would have ended up raping you.'

'Not rape, my love,' she corrected softly, shyly. 'I doubt if I would have fought you at all. Except for when you accused me of making advances towards you, of course!'

'Ah, yes,' he nodded wryly. 'That was when I found I wanted nothing better than to hold you—for ever if need be—and that discovery not only made me mad with myself for letting you get under my skin, but it made me even more annoyed with you for being able to affect me so greatly.'

'Because you still believed I was conniving, and conscienceless, and all those other things you charged me with being?'

He sighed heavily, his expression remorseful. 'Partly, I'm sorry to say, but in the main because you had somehow managed to acquire the unfortunate habit—from my standpoint—of using those beautiful eyes of yours to let me know just exactly what a rotten heel I was being, whereupon I immediately wanted to strike back and hurt you all the more.'

'And succeeded quite admirably on a number of occasions,' she recalled ruefully.

'Don't remind me!' His plea was made in tones of self-disgust. 'Can you ever forgive me?'

She dimpled mischievously. 'I'll try, and especially if you continue saying nice things about me. It makes such a pleasant change.'

'Minx! I knew you were going to be trouble from the moment I first saw you, sitting there defying me before I even knew who you were,' he glowered at her mock-ferociously. 'It would have served you right if I had sacked you when I was considering it.'

'When was that?' she gasped in astonishment. He had always seemed so firm in his conviction that he could make her resign that it had never occurred to her that he might have contemplated dismissal as a means of getting rid of her.

'Your first afternoon here,' he divulged with a smile for her amazement. 'If you remember, you made a somewhat sarcastic remark as I left the office.'

'Only because you'd just done the same to me.'

'Mmm, but fair play was the last thing I had on my mind at the time, and when I walked back into the room I thought, "To hell with waiting for her to resign", and I fully intended firing you on the spot.'

'So why didn't you?' she frowned perplexedly.

'Because, my darling, that was the first time I fell victim to your eyes. They were so wide and so nervous, and such a glorious colour, all I could do was to stare at them, fascinated, until I'd completely forgotten what I damned well meant to say!' ironically.

Debra burst into delightful laughter. 'Are you sorry?' Those same violet eyes flirted with him outrageously.

'You might be if you tempt me too far!' he vowed drily.

'Yes, Mac,' she acceded in pretended submissiveness.

'Uh-uh!' he vetoed repressively. 'I've told you before, only my friends call me that.'

Her glance turned reproachful. 'And doesn't a wife-to-be qualify as one of those?'

'*Male* friends,' he enunciated with a smile.

'But that's what Anthea calls you,' she protested.

One well shaped brow quirked sardonically. 'And did I say I liked it? I can assure you there's quite a few things Anthea says that I don't agree with.'

He wasn't the only one, but with his arms securely around her she could afford to be magnanimous. 'I felt quite sorry for her this afternoon. You were so ruthlessly blunt.'

'Was I?' He seemed unconcerned whether he had been or not. 'I thought I did extremely well in controlling my temper, and that she was lucky to get off as lightly as she did. Apart from the fact that there's only one female I want making overtures to me, I certainly wasn't going to permit her to vent her spite on you.'

His reasons were rewarded by a pleased smile and a sigh of utter contentment. 'Up until then I'd been under the impression she was your girl-friend,' she confessed, happily now.

'Thanks!' His arms tightened menacingly and a crooked tilt formed at the corner of his mouth. 'That really says a lot for my judgment.'

'Well, I wasn't to know,' she half laughed, half pouted. 'I mean, she used to carry on as if she was, and I certainly didn't see you doing anything to discourage her.'

'The same as you weren't exactly struggling to escape Paul?'

'There wasn't any need!' she retorted. 'You always saw to that for me.'

'Rather well too most times, I thought,' he grinned impenitently. 'You really didn't get to see much of him at all, did you?'

'No!' She wrinkled her nose at him wryly. 'But was that because you just wanted to make life less enjoyable for me, or—or ...'

'Or because I was too damned jealous to let him near you? I'll give you one clue,' he volunteered huskily as he lowered his head to take possession of her lips with absorbing efficiency.

When he raised it again all thoughts of Paul had fled from Debra's mind, but there was a teasing light in her eyes as she advised, 'Er—I seem to be having a little difficulty with my translation. Do you think you could repeat that clue for me, please?'

The tender curve of his mouth was a caress in itself. 'As often as you wish, my love,' he promised.

FREE!
Romance Treasury

**A beautifully bound,
value-packed,
three-in-one
volume of romance!**

FREE!

**A hardcover Romance Treasury volume
containing 3 treasured works of romance
by 3 outstanding Harlequin authors . . .**

**. . . as your introduction to Harlequin's
Romance Treasury subscription plan!**

Romance Treasury

**. . . almost 600 pages of exciting romance reading
every month at the low cost of $5.97 a volume!**

A wonderful way to collect many of Harlequin's most beautiful love
stories, all originally published in the late '60s and early '70s.
Each value-packed volume, bound in a distinctive gold-embossed
leatherette case and wrapped in a colorfully illustrated dust jacket,
contains . . .

- 3 full-length novels by 3 world-famous authors of romance fiction
- a unique illustration for every novel
- the elegant touch of a delicate bound-in ribbon bookmark . . .
  and much, much more!

Romance Treasury

. . . for a library of romance you'll treasure forever!

Complete and mail today the FREE gift certificate and subscription
reservation on the following page.